THE QUEEN'S
GIFT BOOK

From the painting by
William Llewellyn, A.R.A.,
in Buckingham Palace

THE QUEEN'S GIFT BOOK

HONI·SOIT·QUI·MAL·Y·PENSE

IN AID OF
QUEEN MARY'S CONVALESCENT
AUXILIARY HOSPITALS
FOR SOLDIERS AND SAILORS WHO
HAVE LOST THEIR LIMBS IN THE WAR

HODDER AND STOUGHTON
LONDON · NEW YORK · TORONTO

FOREWORD
BY
JOHN GALSWORTHY

THE place I came to seemed a green and fortunate haven for the battered. Ah! Ships you can refit, making them as good as new; but these four hundred men in their blueish hospital garb and their red neckties can never be made as good as new. You can only make shift for them, and do your best. Legs and arms, legs and arms—they all want one or the other, and some want both.

They have just passed to dinner—a long procession—in wheelchairs, on crutches, or walking strangely, the freshly fitted leg thrown out a little apart, stiffly as yet; or seemingly quite whole and active men, till you observe they have only one arm. One of them has lost two legs and an arm, another an arm and a leg and an eye. So they go, young, pathetically strong—cheerful fellows, wonderful fellows, stoics. Some one says: "They're not worrying; that's Tommy all over—never thinks of to-morrow." Well, it would seem the better ground-philosophy for armless men, legless men, who by no measure of thought for to-morrow will ever have two arms or legs, or even perhaps one, again.

And yet—they must and shall have a to-morrow! That is the object and policy of this Haven called Queen Mary's Auxiliary Convalescent Hospitals, in Roehampton. Certainly crippled men could hardly have better quarters, attention, and grub than they get here (the Staff eat exactly what the patients do—such is the matron's admirable plan); but these one-legged, one-winged birds of passage stay but a few weeks or days. An ever-lengthening flock of the maimed waits for empty perches; and so, as soon as 'to-morrow' is fairly in sight, each passes out and on, to make way for a waiting comrade. The real business is to fit them properly with new limbs, and with a new future, while they are here.

How far can this be done?

3

An instrument-maker shows me legs—not very heavy, much lighter actually, but of course heavier in effect, than the lost limbs.

"How far does it show—say, with an amputation below the knee ? "

The instrument-maker walks a few paces and comes back.

" You can judge for yourself—I've got one on."

" I should never have known it."

" No ? It depends on the man. Some will always show it—others——"

" A matter of temperament ! "

" That's right."

" But—above the knee ? "

" Charlie, just walk across, will you ? "

A young man walks. You would say he had a bad corn, or a weak knee—not more.

" That," says the instrument-maker, " comes of getting the limb exactly right. And for that it's vital to have the man right here with you a bit at the start, so as you can watch it, pare away what's wrong, and get it to fit him O.K. And another thing I'll tell you : The better the instrument—and, unfortunately, the more expensive—the more comfortable it'll be."

" It's not mere polish, then, that adds to the expense ? "

" No, *sir* ; it's extra efficiency—skill and time spent on it."

" And does it worry a man much when it's first put on ? "

" Well, it's not just an addition to his comfort ; but he soon gets to feel all right with it. This is what we cover them with—calf-skin. I should like you to see the officer that's going to have this leg ; he wears it A 1."

This then is the importance of precisely the " just " limb.

And the second part of the work here—the placing of the maimed on the path of a new utility and hope, the fitting of him with his to-morrow ? It goes very well, they say—very well, so far. It is up to the public to see that it goes well to the end.

Passing back through the new wooden wards, twenty or thirty beds in each, and two stoves—very scrupulous, comfortable, airy ; through the recreation rooms—small billiard tables, chess, dominoes, plenty of books, and heaps of papers, I sit down in a wheel-chair vacated by one with left leg gone and right leg badly damaged, who has got into a more solid chair alongside, to read a magazine. Here is a bit of irony—perhaps the only bit of its kind in the whole of the two hospitals.

This one was damaged not by man, but by that act of God—the falling of a rock; and the very next week his battalion went to the front, and he was the only man left behind. He cannot be more than twenty-five, in radiant health, eyes full of light and life, and that expression of perfected patience which, above everything, touches the heart. He has read a good deal, he says, since he was in hospital. He will have his leg on Monday; but as to his future, he does not know as yet.

I go out on to the lawn. Under a light-grey sky, between the terrace of the big house and some cedar trees whose dark branches lie so still and flat on the windless autumn air, they are punting a football. A little man in a Scotch cap, with a pale brown, keen-jawed face, prefers to lift his crutches, jump clean off the ground with his one leg, kick the ball hard, and return to earth. He looks as if he has been a good player in his time—a half-back probably. They have very likely all been good players; and now a kind of incredulous amusement at their infirmity seems to possess them, whether they play or whether they look on. Watching the spread, the quick intricate flourish, and trail of their crutches, their laughing utter abandonment to the moment, one cannot help thinking of winged and lamed jackdaws sporting together; but no cheerful jackdaw ever had such pluck as this.

The tales that might be heard here would fill many volumes, if one had but the gift of expression. Here, for instance, is a man who, with arm and leg broken and one eye blinded, lay out on the field two days, and having just missed being prodded to death by one of Culture's children, was thrown into a barn with ten others, till our men came along and rescued them. Yes, that everlasting fellow is here now, waiting for his limbs and his ' to-morrow,' making less of his past suffering and his future fate than many a man in the old days when a penny was added to the income tax.

Here is one who, having lost a leg and been wounded I forget where besides, lay, together with two other maimed and helpless fellows, nine days in a ruined farm with no food, and for water a puddle with a dead sheep in it, to which one of the three only was able to crawl. As the doctor put it : " The puddle was sustaining—full of body." Anyway, he lived, and is waiting for his limb and his future.

Beside me, watching the football, is a man in a wheel-chair with both feet gone—frost-bite. He knows as little as I whether all that frost-bite was necessary in our latitudes, even in the conditions that prevailed last winter. . . . However, here he is in his wheel-chair, waiting for feet, and his future, and laughing when the man in the Scotch cap leaves the earth to kick the ball.

The doctor, the lady superintendent, the matron, the nurses, all tell us that these four hundred are not down-hearted, not even in their spare and lonely moments. Cockney and Yorkshireman, Celt and Canadian, West-countryman and Midlander, sailor or soldier, hardly a man of them downhearted. It's very wonderful, very grand, very touching. They draw strength, no doubt, from all being in the same boat, from their country's gratitude, from the admiring interest they feel they are inspiring; but allowing for all this, their hearts must be of oak right through.

But this is what I would be saying: True, that for the moment, and for the long coming months, perhaps years, that the war will last, even for a spell after Peace has come, the hearts and minds of all— crippled or not—will be filled and sustained by the thought of the danger to be overcome, the duties to be fulfilled, and the issues at stake. But Time strides on, and Time is a great leveller, making all things small to eyes turned backward, laying low the past, however high, with the pressure of the present's poignancy and of the future's hopes and fears. To us, who do not in this war leave behind some actual part of ourselves, our limbs, our sight, our speech, our hearing— to us, looking back, the mountainous happenings of to-day will acquire a dream-like quality and sink in the distance, or in new lights attain quite different shapes and values. Then will the haloes round the maimed grow dim to us, the consoling, grateful glow in hearts die down, and a cold wind blow round these half-wrecked lives. But in the hearts of the maimed memory will not fade nor from their seared fibre disablement depart. They will be limping monuments of a half-buried war, no longer upheld by the admiration of their countrymen, nor much by their own consciousness of duty done, but having to make good as best they can with an unremarked gallantry greater than any they showed in the wet, shell-searched trenches, or charging a storm of bullets—greater, because it must last so long—all the rest of their lives. To us others this war will in due time come to be but a terrific episode; but *they* will pay perpetual price. After the first flush of honour and attention, it is hard to see what pennyworth of real compensation Fate has in store for the maimed. Pensions? Yes, pensions! Into that paradise of beer and skittles the legless or armless no doubt enter; and a low-geared imagination will try to tell them that they are blessed, or to assure them that they are " spoiled "; but something in them will ever say, and something in you and me will ever echo—"No number of shillings a week, not even twenty-five, can make up this loss "; no more than daily hempseed makes up to the caged bullfinch for the loss of his wings, or guaranteed free meals to a leopard for his imprisonment. It is the spirit of a man that suffers when he can no longer express the bounding energy within him. And yet, perhaps, after all there is one deep compensation for those who can attain to it. For surely to have to conquer day by day a hundred little difficulties that one with all his limbs knows not, to have to bear stoically year by year the loss of full expression, must fortify the will-power; and by will-power men attain full stature. Is it a forlorn hope that sees these maimed comrades transfigured—with heads up, marching down the years in spite of Fate, finer-spirited, stronger-souled than ordinary men? That is, at any rate, the vision before this Haven where they have put in to be refitted.

To give the maimed back the best equivalent for what they have lost, the best mechanical substitutes for shattered limbs, and such openings in life as shall suit their altered outlook, keep hope and self-respect in them, keep them eager and full-lived men in that far future when the drums and fifes have long been still, and their very echo is but a ghost of unreal sound,—to do all this, in so far as it can be done, is the problem and the task before Queen Mary's Convalescent Auxiliary Hospitals.

And this book is designed to help the work. 'Tis in the nature of a hat passed round, into which, God send, many hundred thousand coins may be poured! But a book can only hope to raise a portion of the money wanted. More, more, and—alas !—ever more will be needed, not of our generosity, but of our consciences, till no single one of all those who, by giving of their flesh and bone, have helped to save the flesh and bone of Britain and the fair name of Britain, can say with truth : " I gave that bit of me, and I'm crippled for life. I thought they'd do what they could for me, after. But you see—they didn't."

In the name of the Lady, dear to England, who watches over this work, it is my privilege to ask that we fail not our honour in this matter. However little these Stoics make of it now—theirs is an abiding sacrifice, an abiding grief. We are deep in their debt. All that we can, shall we not cheerfully repay?

JOHN GALSWORTHY.

CONTENTS

HE COMES! was originally published in "The Cornhill Magazine"; THE SOOT FAIRIES in "New Book of the Fairies"; PORTRAIT OF A LADY in "Sketches in Lavender, Blue and Green"; THE DANE'S BREECHIN' in "All on the Irish Shore"; THE CUBHOOD OF WAHB in "The Biography of a Grizzly"; THE LITTLE GOATHERD in "Eleanor"; and we have to thank the Proprietors of "The Cornhill Magazine," the Joint Committee of Henry Frowde and Hodder & Stoughton, Messrs. Longmans, Green & Co., and Messrs. Smith, Elder & Co. for permission to include these contributions in THE QUEEN'S GIFT BOOK.

HIS MAJESTY THE KING.

*From the painting by A. S. Cope, R.A., in Buckingham Palace,
presented to the Queen by the Marys of the Empire,
as a Coronation gift, June, 1911*

THE QUEEN'S
GIFT BOOK

THE PLEASURES OF READING

BY THE RT. HON. ARTHUR JAMES BALFOUR

THE best method of guarding against the danger of reading what is useless is to read only what is interesting,—a truth which will seem a paradox to a whole class of readers, fitting objects of our commiseration, who may be often recognised by their habit of asking some adviser for a list of books, and then marking out a scheme of study in the course of which all are to be conscientiously perused. These unfortunate persons apparently read a book principally with the object of getting to the end of it. They reach the word *Finis* with the same sensation of triumph as an Indian feels who strings a fresh scalp to his girdle. They are not happy unless they mark by some definite performance each step in the weary path of self-improvement. To begin a volume and not to finish it would be to deprive themselves of this satisfaction; it would be to lose all the reward of their earlier self-denial by a lapse from virtue at the end. To skip, according to their literary code, is a species of cheating; it is a mode of obtaining credit for erudition on false pretences—a plan by which the advantages of learning are surreptitiously obtained by those who have not won them by honest toil. But all this is quite wrong. In matters literary, works have no saving efficacy. He has only half learnt the art of reading who has not added to it the even more refined accomplishments of skipping and of skimming; and the first step has hardly been taken in the direction of making literature a pleasure until interest in the subject, and not a desire to spare (so to speak) the author's feelings, or to accomplish an appointed task, is the prevailing motive of the reader.

□   □   □   □

I am deliberately of opinion that it is the pleasures and not the profits, spiritual or temporal, of literature which most require to be preached in the ear of the ordinary reader. I hold, indeed, the faith that all such pleasures minister to the development of much that is best in man—mental and moral; but the charm is broken and the object lost if the remote consequence is consciously pursued to the exclusion of the immediate end. It will not, I suppose, be denied that the beauties of nature are at least as well qualified to minister to our higher needs as are the beauties of literature. Yet we do not say that we are going to walk to the top of such and such a hill in order to drink in "spiritual sustenance." We say we are going to look at the view. And I am convinced that this, which is the natural and simple way of considering literature as well as nature, is also the true way.

From the Address delivered by Mr. Balfour as Lord Rector of St. Andrews University, December 10, 1887.

THE NEW DRAMATIST

By J. M. Barrie

Drawings by
Lewis Baumer

EVEN before we were engaged I knew of Charles's delicious literary ambition. He meant to write a play—not an ordinary play, but the one for which all the best people have been calling for years. We felt a little self-conscious when we read those demands for a real play, and a little nervous also, lest some one should go and write it before Charles had arranged the preliminaries. I was the chief preliminary, but there were others connected with business, for by day Charles is only a clerk, though a much-valued one, and has to give to a ledger many hours that really ought to be at the service of the public.

I sometimes sighed over this, because it prevented his beginning to write the witty thing at once; but he was so brave. "You will find," he said cheerily, "that the big artistic work has nearly always been done by men who seemed to have no spare time in which to do it. Obstacles were made only to be overthrown. I am firmly convinced that what is in a man will out."

As soon as summer arrived he was to begin.

Charles glowed with quiet fire when he spoke to me of the play, and he told me a number of things about it, quite the most delightful of which was that he would never really have understood women if he had not known me. "There are to be little bits of the heroine," he would say, "which will simply be chipped off you." And often when he lapsed into silence, with his eyes fixed on me, I had the exquisite feeling that he was chipping.

Our engagement was not of long duration, for Charles coaxed me to church in such words as these: "Time is getting on, and I can't settle down to the play until we are married."

We built our new house, as one may say, round the play, giving it one entire room, with all the pretty things that we felt it needed, and so we had to be rather skimpy in the furnishing of the other rooms. I don't know which of us was the more anxious to make sacrifices for the play; the same thought leapt to both minds at once, "Yes, truly the drawing-room settee is a dream, but let us rather buy that study table with the secret drawer; it will so

10

help me (you) at your (my) work, and once the play is launched we can have a surfeit of settees."

"Every evening," I told him, "you will find your manuscript (we pronounced it MS.; I do so love that word) lying on the table waiting for you, and a pen with a new nib in it. "Dear Dora," he replied, though that is not my name.

"But you mustn't work too hard at it," I insisted; "you must have fixed hours, and at a certain time, say at 10 o'clock, I shall simply order you to cease writing for the night."

He saw the wisdom of this, but questioned its practicability. "You don't know," he said (he was always a great reader), "how the hours rush by on wings when one is in the throes of composition. I shall often feel when ten strikes that I have just begun."

I vowed I should come behind him at ten and snatch the pen from his hand.

"Every Saturday evening," he promised, "I shall read to you what I have written during the week."

We were married on a September day, and quite a valuable part of the honeymoon was spent in talk about the play and its heroine. I got him to promise to make her a brunette in case she was *too* like. Often from the movement of his fingers I knew he was yearning to be writing, and nothing proved the depth of his affection for me more than his not yielding to temptation. I sometimes told him so, and he admitted it, saying quaintly that I read him like a play.

Conceive us at home in our dear little house in Clapham.

"Will you begin the play this evening?" I asked him, as soon as we had run up and down the stairs a few times, and peeped into all the rooms sharply, just to take the darlings by surprise.

His wish was to do so, but he felt that it would be wiser to settle down first. "I shall keep off it for a week," he said firmly.

"Please, not for my sake," I begged him, for I had watched his hungry look at the study table.

"For your sake entirely," he said, in his dear way.

"But isn't it a pity to waste any more time?"

He did just a little surprise me.

"There is no such violent hurry," he said rather testily; it was the first time I had ever heard that note in his voice except when he was speaking to a cabman, and we don't speak to them often.

I suppose he noticed my surprise (he notices everything), for he added, "The time won't be wasted; I can be thinking."

"But you have thought so long," I said.

It was silly of me.

"Isn't the lack of thought," he retorted, "acknowledged to be the curse of the drama?"

We had, of course, a good many callers at this time, and rather imprudently I told them about the play. They were so interested, and continued to be so interested, that I regret this now.

When the week had become a fortnight, I insisted on leaving Charles alone in the study after dinner. He looked rather gloomy, but I filled the ink-bottles (one with red ink, because he likes his MS. to be so neat) and put the large sheets of paper before him. As my share of the work (this had been planned during the honeymoon), I wrote the title of the play, which had been fixed on long before, and a most tantalising title it is, though I was sworn to secrecy, because if divulged it might be stolen (such is the state of the copyright laws). I also wrote the words " Act I.," kissed the empty place beneath and another blank spot on Charles's head, and handed him the pen. My poor little part was done. Charles took the pen, but he did not thank me. I don't mean that he was unkind (he is never that), but he certainly did not thank me.

An hour afterwards I slipped into the study with a cup of tea. He was sitting by the fire with the cat on his knee and an odd expression on his face, as if the cat were his only friend.

"You are not sleeping, Charles?" I asked, before I saw the cat.

"Sleeping!" he said, rather indignantly, as if I had charged him with some crime. "No, I am thinking."

"Again!" I exclaimed thoughtlessly.

He asked me, really almost tartly, what I meant by "again."

I said I only meant that he had not written anything yet.

"I was just going to begin when you came in," he said. "I shall begin as soon as I have drunk this tea."

But when I returned at ten to insist on his stopping work, he was still nursing the cat. I didn't like to look at the MS.

Next evening Charles said he felt a curious disinclination for writing, and thought he would take a night off. I must have looked disappointed, for, though he is the gentlest of men, he flared up.

"I can't be eternally writing," he growled; but fortunately I like him growling.

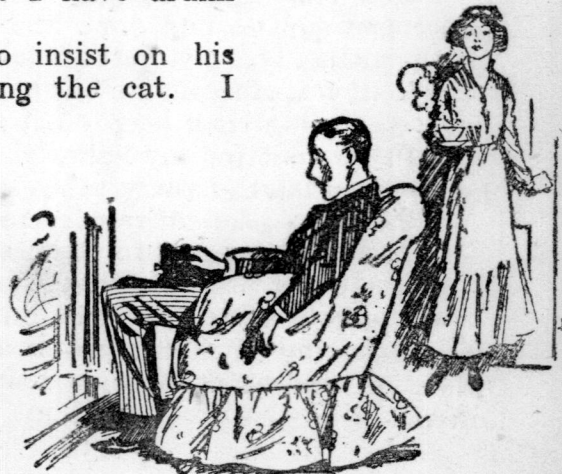

"But you haven't done anything at all yet."

Of course this was inconsiderate of me, and I think he took it rather sweetly. All he said was, "Don't you think that is rather an ungenerous way of putting it?"

"But you always spoke as if the work would be such a pleasure to you."

"Have I said that it is not a pleasure? If you knew anything of literary history, you would know that there are times when the most industrious writers cannot pen a line. My present feeling is merely a proof that I have the artistic temperament, and surely it is all to the good to find that I have that."

"Still," I said diffidently, "they must all make a beginning some time."

"Undoubtedly," he said, "and I shall make mine to-morrow."

To-morrow came, however, without finding him in the study. He almost implored me to let him spend the evening hanging the bedroom pictures.

I said I could not possibly drag him away from the play.

"You are in a most uncommon desperate hurry to see me shut myself up with that play," he said testily. It was the first time he had called it "that play."

"You spoke as if you were so anxious to begin it."

"So I am. Have I ever said I was not?"

He marched off to the study, banging the drawing-room door. An hour or so afterwards I took him tea, and somehow I knew that between the rattle of the cup and the opening of the door he had sprung from the couch to the study table, where I found him pen in hand. I noticed also that an arm was raised as a barricade against my seeing the MS.

"How are you getting on?" I said, nevertheless, out of sheer niceness; and this time he had the effrontery to reply, "Excellently, oh, excellently."

And yet except on matters of art there never was a more scrupulously truthful man. The artistic temperament again, I suppose.

He drank his tea so slowly, that it could only have been because he was reluctant to reach the bottom of the cup. I tried to look over the barricade, but it at once rose higher.

"I shall come in to stop you at ten sharp," I said, preparing to go.

He tried to be appealing and brazen at the same time. "I think I have perhaps done enough for one night," he said; "I mustn't overdo it."

"But how much have you done?"

He made an evasive reply that quality was better than quantity, and muttered something about writers' cramp.

" If you would like me to be your amanuensis——" I began, but he would not hear of that.

" Do read me the opening scene," I begged him, but he preferred that I should wait till Saturday. When Saturday came, he was not " in the mood." He was not even in the mood for writing ; he was in the mood for mending the kitchen clock. He became quite a handy man about the house, except in the study.

So the play-writing went on.

One morning I counted the blank sheets, and found they were just as I had placed them on the table the evening before. He had not even torn any of them up that night. Thus it went on for a week or two, with this difference. He either suspected that I counted the sheets, or thought I might take it into my head to do so ; he therefore locked away the MS. (as we still called it) in the secret drawer. I had a key which could unlock that drawer, and here is a really lovely little story about myself, complete in six words : I never did unlock the drawer.

His new way of avoiding Saturday was to say that it would be better not to read any of the play aloud to me until a whole act was finished.

Then the study became, I suppose, so detestable to him that he had to take stronger action. He came home one day from the City with a pair of spectacles.

"Yes, it does seem a pity," he admitted, when I shrank from the horrid things, " but I must take care of my eye-sight ; and what with all this writing by incandescent light——"

Here he paused to let me say something, and I knew so well by this time what he wanted me to say, and I am a good wife, so I gulped and said it. The upshot was a decision (to please me) to postpone any further work on the play, or to defer beginning the play (I forget how we put it) until the long days set in. May was the month

I suggested for resumption, but he insisted on April.

April arrived (the middle of it), and I said I thought it would be a good omen if he resumed work on the 23rd, which was the birthday of another dramatist, as stated in my calendar.

"You are eternally talking about that play," he snapped; which was almost unkind of him, for the play was the one subject now tabooed in our little home by unspoken mutual agreement.

"Because you used to be so enthusiastic about it," I said.

"I am as enthusiastic as ever, but I can't be always writing the play."

"We have now been married seven months, and you haven't shown me a line yet." I said "shown me a line," not "written a line," you observe.

He retired to the study in dudgeon, and sat staring at the MS., as I daresay a hen may regard an addled egg. My chief feeling about Charles is usually pride, but I felt very sorry for him that night when he broke down and told me everything. His play has a splendid plot, with rippling comedy scenes and some of the subtlest touches of character (especially in the heroine). It is absolutely the play for which every one has been calling. This I knew from the first, for he had again and again regaled me with unwritten tit-bits. What then was the trouble? It was this: Charles simply could not find a beginning for his play. All the rest he knew, but he could not get begun.

It had been very noble of him to try to save me pain by keeping this wretched little trouble from me for so long, and I hope I was a good wife to him that evening.

"It does seem unfair," I said, "that such a small thing should stand between us and fame, but there are sweeter things than fame (he knew to what I was referring), and my advice is that you abandon the play altogether. After all," I said severely, "the country has the plays it deserves."

Somehow that made Charles look at me very wofully, and I implored him to tell me why, and at last he admitted that it was because he feared I would not admire him now as much as I used to do.

The idea! But it made me cry.

Soon he was happy again, and he even said he would have another bout with the play, but not that evening.

I was in his confidence now, and he let me try to think out a beginning. I thought of a lovely one: the curtain to rise on two servants dusting and talking about the other characters. But, strange to tell, I found that this was the very beginning Charles had thought of him-

self and abandoned because it had been already used by some hateful playwright of the Restoration period. Thus I was no great help, but our thinking of the same beginning is a delightful proof that Charles and I are not twain, but one.

That summer it was so pleasant to be out of doors, that Charles was little in his study. Sometimes he thought of writing in the orchard, but there was the danger of the MS. being blown away.

The winter was such an usually hard one that his fingers froze if he sat for any length of time at the study table. We often discussed the advisability of pushing the study table nearer the fire.

So many exquisite evenings we had, crouching over the blazing logs, nothing to mar them except the consciousness that Charles should be otherwise engaged.

For ever and ever and ever was the date to which I now wanted him to abandon the work, but he still clung to the idea of resumption at some future time.

"Let us say this day one year hence?" I suggested.

He thought that was too definite.

"Well, then, let us say till an idea strikes you."

He had some objection to that also; I forget now what it was.

We finally decided that he should abandon the "actual writing of the play" until he had had time to look around. I don't know why, but this phrase relieved him very much.

Never since that blessed day has the MS. given us the slightest trouble. The phrase, on the other hand, has been changed several times. It has been "until we move into a more convenient house," and "until we have settled down in the new house," and at present it is, "until the children are older."

For you must not think that Charles has given up the scheme. I have never known him fuller of it than during the last year or two. I notice also that he now speaks of it cheerily to our friends, which, by the way, I have ceased to do.

I love Charles more than ever, though perhaps I know him better now. And I also little play. Never slightingly of it. It cess" to me. Our it was what first together; perhaps riage would never ning. Charles be- tifully, and sustains in the most de- though he may not own (but that re-

love his unborn shall I speak has been a "suc- common interest in brought us close but for it our mar- have had a Begin- gan my play beau- it from act to act lightful ways, be able to begin his mains to be seen).

THE QUEEN'S GIFT BOOK

HIS ROYAL HIGHNESS THE PRINCE OF WALES.

From the painting by A. S. Cope, R.A., in Buckingham Palace

JILL'S CAT
By E. F. Benson
Drawings by
Harry Rountree

WHERE Jill's cat came from I have no idea: she just came, like the summer or the swallows, from somewhere else. I first set eyes on her on returning home from dinner late one night in August, when windows had been left wide for the sake of air, and found her neatly and comfortably coiled up in an arm-chair in my sitting-room, very fast asleep. Naturally therefore I opened the door of this room which gave on to the garden, and advanced upon her clapping my hands and emitting loud and terrifying noises in order to drive her out, for I was not then aware that I wanted Jill's cat. But she merely twitched a drowsy ear, stretched out one paw with extreme languor and looked at me with one half-opened yellow eye, as if to say "It is surely too late to play about: let me go to sleep again."

But I still did not want her to go to sleep in my house, and though I regretted having to violate the ancient and sacred claims of hospitality, it was impossible to respect them so far as to give a home to any stray cat that might happen to come along and enter my sitting-room. So, already hesitating but firm in purpose, I took her up respectfully with both hands, intending to put her feet into the garden and shut the door. But the moment I touched her she set up a loud tea-kettle purr, as if to welcome even in her somnolence the touch of a friend, and licked with a rough pink tongue the hand that was near her head.

Now for a cat to show such marks of confidence to a stranger, is to the stranger, if he is but the merest neophyte in cat-matters, an affair vastly complimentary. In nine cases out of ten a stray cat would have bounced angrily from the room at being disturbed by the rude noises I had made, and have certainly woke up, suspicious and distrustful on being touched. Not so Jill's cat: she said just, "Oh, are you still there? How nice? Shan't we go to sleep again?" This was certainly a very clever cat that made me feel so agreeable a person to cats, and I told myself (though I do not think my inmost mind really believed it) that I would definitely drive this pleasant but unbidden guest away in the morning. So I left Jill's cat in possession of the chair, and she continued purring till I left the room. Probably she knew that she had already begun to make good her position in the new home she had adopted.

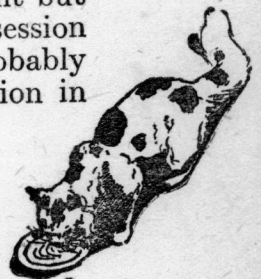

3

Most cats are absolutely tactless; they are easily bored (showing their boredom in a manner which it is perfectly impossible to construe otherwise), and have the rooted conviction that the human inhabitants of the world were created solely to amuse, feed, and shelter them. In all these respects Jill's cat was different from her race. She had all the tact which was left out of the composition of other cats, and when the housemaid came into the room next morning to do her dusting, Jill's cat hailed her at once as an old and valued friend, and went to meet her with little cries of welcome, making a poker of her tail. Naturally the housemaid thawed before these exquisite manners, and, instead of turning her out at once, as she (and I also the night before) had meant to do, she took her down into the kitchen to give her a saucer of milk before putting her out on to her pilgrim's way. Jill's cat was hungry, and with the dainty eagerness of her race began to appropriate her breakfast. But, half-way through it, she suddenly froze into stone, but for the end of a twitching tail, and regarded with the blazing eyes of the huntress the wainscoting opposite. Next moment a mouse was pinned by the talons of her velvet paws; the moment after there was no mouse externally visible at all. By that piece of work she insinuated herself into the heart of my cook (as well as enjoying herself very much) and not only showed that she had tact, but that she was going to work for her living, instead of expecting everybody to amuse her. Then, having deposited the poor mouse's tail, which she did not feel disposed to eat, at the cook's feet, as a small oblation showing respect and homage, she finished her milk very neatly.

Certainly Jill's cat had shown excellent diplomacy (I wish the conduct of affairs at Constantinople had been in her hands); but there was a far more critical and hazardous passage in front of her than establishing good relations with the cook, the housemaid, and me. For she was not yet aware that the household really revolved round none of us, but round Jill; and Jill, being young, was capricious, and being a fox-terrier might possible object to the presence of a cat, or rejoice in its presence merely as being a quarry to pursue. Jill had slept that night as usual on various parts of my bed and me, and came down with me in the morning. I had forgotten for the moment all about the cat, and, an hour later, entered the dining-room for breakfast with Jill circling round me, and making short runs at my boots, which, so she had lately ascertained, on what grounds I know not, were some sort of enemy which must be constantly growled at and attacked. Thus then, heedless of cats, we entered the dining-room.

There on the hearthrug, symmetrically arranged round one hind-leg which stuck up in the middle of her like a flagstaff, sat Jill's cat, diligently employed on her morning

toilet. The scurry of our entrance interrupted her ablutions, and, looking up with a calm and trustful eye, she saw Jill. I had one moment of horrified suspense as to whether the cat would go for Jill or Jill for the cat, and the flying of fur or hair seemed imminent and inevitable. But Jill's cat was equal, more than equal to the occasion : she dominated the occasion instantly, and never have I seen the " right thing " so quickly comprehended or so unhesitatingly performed. With one swift, stealthy movement she had concealed herself underneath a corner of the table-cloth which hung down to the ground, and a white paw tipped with black was gingerly put out with little dabs and jerks and mysterious tremblings of the table-cloth.

Now how, except by the possession of tact that amounted to genius, should that cat have known that Jill must be instantly conciliated, or how have guessed that the one thing irresistible to Jill was an agency concealed under a rug or the corner of a curtain which made known its presence by mysterious jerkings and tremblings ? But she did know it, and, before I could snatch Jill up to avert the impending catastrophe, no catastrophe impended any longer, and the two were rapturously engaged in a gorgeous game of hide-and-seek behind curtains, table-legs, fenders, the *Daily Telegraph*, and chairs—wherever, in fact, there was the possibility of making ambushes and causing mysterious and secret stirrings. So destiny shapes our ends, and from that moment the stranger of the night before had entered on a new existence and become Jill's cat.

Both in body and mind Jill's cat was strong and kind and square. Apparently nature had intended her to be white originally, but had then changed her mind and dabbed her with fortuitous black patches like a nursery rocking-horse. Physically, but for her firmness, she was undistinguished ; it was in mind that she so excelled. Not only was she Jill's cat, but Jill's governess, for Jill, being young and remarkably attractive, was flirtatiously inclined, and through the railings of the front garden which gave on a public road she was apt to behave in a rather common manner with the young gentlemen of the neighbourhood. The railings were too narrow to admit of her squeezing her plump little body through them (she tried once, and stuck, rousing the entire parish by the shrillness of her lamentations), and she had to content her feminine instincts with putting her head through, and indiscriminately kissing any dog who felt disposed to receive her caresses. But Jill's cat (in the rôle of governess) instantly thwarted these unladylike proceedings, for whenever she observed Jill trotting down to the garden railings and inserting her head through them to

kiss everybody, she would follow, and from the vantage-ground of the gatepost turn herself into a perfect demon of spitting rage, thus distracting Jill's indiscriminate friends from love, and filling their hearts with war. One particular terrier who was an assiduous loafer in what we may call Jill's amatorium was the object of her especial aversion, and the language she considered it necessary to use to him was more responsible, I believe, for the blistering of the paint on the gate than the weeks of that hot summer.

Jill's cat had a perfect mania for work, and her work consisted in catching anything that was alive. Within three days of her arrival I am convinced there was no mouse left in the precincts, and, having cleared the place of them, she turned her attention to birds, butterflies, and snails. I regretted her industry among the birds, though, as a matter of fact, she did not catch many; but it was quite impossible to stop it, or the belief that no living thing except Jill, herself, and human beings must set foot in house or garden. It took her some time to discover that snails were alive, owing to the pitiable tardiness of their movements, but that fact once grasped, they took their place amid the spoils of the chase, and she brought them as presents to her cook, or Jill, or me. This generosity had its disadvantages, for Jill, like other children, was fond of collections, and liked concealing small objects of various kinds in the folds of the blanket in her basket. There one day I found two dead unfledged birds, a snail, and portions of what had once been a white butterfly. These no doubt were all presents from her cat.

Her work, together with sudden excursions to the garden-railing to swear at the dogs of the neighbourhood, used to take most of the morning; that over, she cleaned herself (for it was clearly a waste of time to do so until the house-work was finished) and she was then at leisure to play with Jill till lunch-time. Then came the desolating moment of the day, for Jill went for her walk, and her cat sat gazing down the road from the gatepost to wait for her return. Evening came and they slept together in Jill's basket, after a wild romp in which they lay entangled and kicked each other in the face to show their deep and unalterable regard.

A year passed, and then an event occurred which for the time completely puzzled Jill's cat, for Jill became the mother of four puppies, and in a moment changed from being a flighty and playful young woman into a savage and suspicious mother who would allow no one to go near the wood-shed. All this burst upon her cat like a bolt from the blue, for, strolling into the wood-shed on the morning the puppies were born, ready to play, she had to fly for her life, and seek refuge on the top of the garden-wall, where she crouched, trembling with fright and indignation, and full of astonished wonder at the little white demon, once her friend, who snarled and growled at her from the garden-bed below. For the time Jill's whole nature was changed; there were no more excursions to the railings to kiss indiscriminate gentlemen, and, also, she had neither time nor desire to play with her disconsolate cat. But this fierce access of protective maternity lasted not more than a few days, for she could not substantiate any plot against her puppies, and one afternoon she left the hay-packed box where her family lay, and trotted across the lawn to where sat her cat. The latter, remembering Jill's unprovoked assault, sprang up the trunk of a tree as she approached, and glared distrustfully through the leaves, while Jill whined and whimpered below, and put herself into engaging postures on the grass. Then step by step, yearning for the return of those happy times, but still cautiously, her cat descended to the lowest branch of the tree, and, after a long pause, decided to trust and to forget and to forgive, and took a flying leap on to her friend. Next moment they were kicking each other in the face in the old manner, and making ambushes among the geraniums.

But soon Jill's maternal heart yearned again for the nuzzling noses of her infants, and she ran back to the wood-shed. Then ensued a thrilling piece of animal psychology. Very cautiously and ready to fly, the cat followed and inserted her head and half her body through the doorway.

Inside there was dead silence. Jill was evidently pondering as to whether her cat could be trusted to approach these precious things: then, after a pause, came a little friendly whine of welcome and the cat entered. I followed and looked in. Jill was lying in her box, the four puppies cuddled up against her, and her cat was sitting close by, with wide and wondering eyes. Then she raised one paw gently and delicately, and with it just touched the nearest puppy. Certainly they were live things and so ought to be hunted, but on the other hand they were Jill's. Then, advancing another step, she licked them very gently with the tip of her pink tongue. And Jill approved, and said, "Wuff! Wasn't it clever of me?" and we were all very happy to find that marriage after all had not caused any separation between old friends.

So the mysterious bond of sympathy between the two only grew stronger instead of being broken, and Jill's cat became a sort of aunt to the puppies. There was, it is true, one moment

of unfounded suspicion on Jill's part when two out of the four puppies unaccountably vanished, and she was inclined to blame the cat. But this passed, and she took her as joint educator of the

young, now that she no longer wanted a governess herself, and even allowed the beloved ones to go staggering excursions first about the wood-shed, and then over the whole romantic play-ground of the garden under the supervision of their aunt. By degrees, too, the fascination of biting and kicking one's aunt in the face dawned on the infant mind, and all four would lie together, an inextricable mass of paws and little white teeth and pink tongues.

The road just outside the gate was a long straight level, much haunted by motor-cars, and it was here that the end came to that strange animal friendship, for one day Jill was run over and killed just outside my house. The " small slain body " was brought in, and, while the grave was being dug underneath the apple-tree, Jill lay there quite still. And as she lay her cat came out of the house, her work being over, and she therefore disengaged and desirous of relaxa-tion. But Jill was not for play that morning, and her cat strolled away again to look at a bird. Then she returned and sat down by her, trying to attract her attention. She dabbed her with a paw, and, finding that did no good, made a feint of running away. But Jill did not follow. By now the grave was ready, and we laid Jill in it, and filled in the earth. . . .

That night I noticed something white sitting under the apple-tree, and, looking more closely, saw that it was Jill's cat sitting on her grave. She would not come into the house, and next morning she had vanished altogether.

Had she gone to seek Jill, I wonder? And in the end will those two gay little spirits find each other again?

DIVUS JOHNSTON
By John Buchan
Drawings by Arch. Webb

"The Emperor assumed the title of *Divus* or Divine, not of his own desire, but because it was forced upon him by a credulous people."—SUETONIUS, *Lives of the Cæsars*.

THIS story, which you may believe or not as you like, was told me by my friend Mr. Peter Thomson of "Jessieville," Maxwell Avenue, Strathbungo, whom I believe to be a man incapable of mendacity, or, indeed, of imagination. He is a prosperous and retired ship's captain, dwelling in the suburbs of Glasgow, who plays two rounds of golf every day of the week, and goes twice every Sunday to a pink, new U.F. Church. You may often see his ample figure, splendidly habited in broadcloth and finished off with one of those square felt hats which are the Scottish emblem of respectability, moving sedately by Mrs. Thomson's side down the avenue of "Balmorals" and "Belle-vues" where dwell the aristocracy of Strathbungo. It was not there that I met him, however, but in a Clyde steamboat going round the Mull, where I spent a comfortless night on my way to a Highland fishing. It was blowing what he called "a wee bit o' wind," and I could not face the odorous bunks which opened on the dining-room. Seated abaft the funnel, in an atmosphere of ham-and-eggs, bilge, and fresh western breezes, he revealed his heart to me, and this I found in it.

□   □   □   □

"About the age of forty"—said Mr. Thomson—"I was captain of the steamer *Archibald McKelvie*, 1,700 tons burthen, belonging to Brock, Rattray & Linklater, of Greenock. We were principally engaged in the China trade, but made odd trips into the Malay Archipelago and once or twice to Australia. She was a handy bit boat, and I'll not deny that I had many mercies vouchsafed to me when I was her skipper. I raked in a bit of salvage now and then, and my trading commission, paid regularly into the British Linen Bank at Maryhill, was mounting up to a fairish sum. I had no objection to Eastern parts, for I had a good constitution and had outgrown the daftnesses of youth. The berth suited me well, I had a decent lot for ship's company, and I would gladly have looked forward to spend-ing the rest of my days by the *Archibald McKelvie*.

"Providence, however, thought otherwise, for He was preparing

23

a judgment against that ship like the kind you read about in books. We were five days out from Singapore shaping our course for the Philippines, where the Americans were then fighting, when we ran into a queer lown sea. Not a breath of air came out of the sky; if you kindled a match the flame wouldna leap, but smouldered like touchwood; and every man's body ran with sweat like a mill-lade. I kenned fine we were in for the terrors of hell, but I hadna any kind of notion how terrible hell could be. First came a wind that whipped away my funnel, like a potato peeling. We ran before it, and it was like the swee-gee we used to play at when we were laddies. One moment the muckle sea would get up on its hinder end and look at you, and the next you were looking at it as if you were on the top of Ben Lomond looking down at Luss. Presently I saw land in a gap of the water, a land with great blood-red mountains, and, thinks I to myself, if we keep up the pace this boat of mine will not be hindered from ending two or three miles inland in somebody's kail-yard. I was just wondering how we would get the *Archibald McKelvie* back to her native element when she saved me the trouble; for she ran dunt on some kind of a rock, and went straight to the bottom.

"I was the only man saved alive, and if you ask me how it happened I don't know. I felt myself choking in a whirlpool; then I was flung through the air and brought down with a smack into deep waters; then I was in the air again, and this time I landed amongst sand and tree-trunks and got a bash on the head which dozened my senses. When I came to it was morning, and the storm had abated. I was lying about half-way up a beach of fine white sand, for the wave that had carried me landwards in its flow had brought me some of the road back in its ebb. All round me was a sort of free-coup—trees knocked to matchwood, dead fish, and birds and beasts, and some boards which I jaloused came from the *Archibald McKelvie*. I had a big bump on my head, but otherwise I was well and clear in my wits, though empty in the stomach and very dowie in the heart. For I knew something about the islands, of which I supposed this to be one. They were either barren wastes, with neither food nor water, or else they were inhabited by the bloodiest cannibals of the archipelago. It looked as if my choice lay between having nothing to eat and being eaten myself.

"I got up, and, after returning thanks to my Maker, went for a walk in the woods. They were full of queer painted birds, and it was an awful job climbing in and out of the fallen trees. By and by I came into an open bit with a burn where I slockened my thirst. It cheered me up, and I was just beginning to think that this was not such a bad island, and looking to see if I could find anything in the nature of cocoanuts, when I heard a whistle like a steam-syren. It was some sort of signal, for the next I knew I was in the grip of a dozen savages, my arms and feet were lashed together, and I was being carried swiftly through the forest.

" It was a rough journey, and the discomfort of that heathen handling kept me from reflecting upon my desperate position. After nearly three hours we stopped, and I saw that we had come to a city. The streets were not much to look at, and the houses were mud and thatch, but on a hillock in the middle stood a muckle temple not unlike a Chinese pagoda. There was a man blowing a horn, and a lot of folk shouting, but I paid no attention, for I was sore troubled with the cramp in my left leg. They took me into one of the huts and made signs that I was to have it for my habitation. They brought me water to wash, and a very respectable dinner, which included a hen and a vegetable not unlike greens. Then they left me to myself and I lay down and slept for a round of the clock.

" I was three days in that hut. I had plenty to eat and the folk were very civil, but they wouldna let me outbye and there was no window to look out of. I couldna make up my mind what they wanted with me. I was a prisoner, but they did not behave as if they bore any malice, and I might have thought I was an honoured guest, but for the guards at the door. Time hung heavy on my hands, for I had nothing to read and no light to read by. I said over all the chapters of the Bible and all the Scots songs I could remember, and I tried to make a poem about my adventures, but I stuck at the fifth line, for I couldna find a rhyme to *McKelvie*.

" On the fourth morning I was awakened by the most deafening din. I saw through the door that the streets were full of folk in holiday clothes, most of them with flowers in their hair and carrying palm branches in their hands. It was like something out of a Bible picture book. After I had my breakfast four lads in long white gowns arrived, and in spite of all my protests they made a bonny spectacle of me. They took off my clothes, me blushing with shame, and rubbed me with a kind of oil that smelt of cinnamon. Then they shaved my chin, and painted on my forehead a

mark like a freemason's. Then they put on me a kind of white night-gown with a red sash round the middle, and they wouldna be hindered from clapping on my head a great wreath of hot-house flowers, as if I was a funeral.

"And then like a thunder-clap I realised my horrible position. *I was* a funeral. I was to be offered up as a sacrifice to some heathen god—an awful fate for a Free-kirk elder in the prime of life.

"I was so paralytic with terror that I never tried to resist. Indeed, it would have done me little good, for outside there were, maybe, two hundred savages, armed and drilled like soldiers. I was put into a sort of palanquin, and my bearers started on a trot with me up the hill to the temple, the whole population of the city running alongside, and singing songs about their god. I was sick with fear, and I durstna look up, for I did not know what awesome sight awaited me.

"At last I got my courage back. 'Peter,' I says to myself, 'be a man. Remember your sainted covenanting forefathers. You have been chosen to testify for your religion, though it's no likely that yon savages will understand what you say.' So I shut my teeth and resolved before I died to make a declaration of my religious principles, and to loosen some of the heathen's teeth with my fists.

"We stopped at the temple door and I was led through a court and into a muckle great place like a barn, with bats flying about the ceiling. Here there were nearly three thousand heathens sitting on their hunkers. They sang a hymn when they saw me, and I was just getting ready for action when my bearers carried me into another place, which I took to be the Holy of Holies. It was about half the size of the first, and at the end of it was a great curtain of leopards' skins hanging from roof to floor. My bearers set me in the middle of the room, and then rolled about on their stomachs in adoration before the curtain. After a bit they finished their prayers and crawled out backwards, and I was left alone in that fearsome place.

"It was the worst experience of my life. I believed that behind the skins there was a horrible idol, and that at any moment a priest with a knife would slip in to cut my throat. You may crack about courage, but I tell you that a man who can wait without a quiver on his murderers in the middle of a gloomy kirk is more than human. I am not ashamed to confess that the sweat ran over my brow, and my teeth were knocking in my head.

"But nothing happened. Nothing, except that as I sat there I began to feel a most remarkable smell. At first I thought the place was on fire. Then I thought it was the kind

of stink called incense that they make in Popish kirks, for I once wandered into a cathedral in Santiago. But neither guess was right, and then I put my thumb on the proper description. It was nothing but the smell of the third-class carriages on the Coatbridge train on a Saturday night after a football match—the smell of plug tobacco smoked in clay pipes that were no just very clean. My eyes were getting accustomed to the light, and I found the place no that dark; and as I looked round to see what caused the smell, I spied something like smoke coming from beyond the top of the curtain.

"I noticed another thing. There was a hole in the curtain, about six feet from the floor, and at that hole as I watched I saw an eye. My heart stood still, for, thinks I, that'll be the priest of Baal who presently will stick a knife into me. It was long ere I could screw up courage to look again, but I did it. And then I saw that the eye was not that of a savage, which would be black and bloodshot. It was a blue eye, and, as I looked, it winked at me.

"And then a voice spoke out from behind the curtain, and this was what it said. It said, 'Godsake, Peter, is it you? And how did ye leave them a' at Maryhill?'

"And from behind the curtain walked a muckle man, dressed in a pink blanket, a great red-headed man, with a clay pipe in his mouth. It was the god of the savages, and who do ye think it was? A man Johnston, who used to bide in the same close as me in Glasgow. . . ."

Mr. Thomson's emotion overcame him, and he accepted a stiff drink from my flask. Wiping away a tear, which may have been of sentiment or of mirth, he continued:

"You may imagine that I was joyful and surprised to see him, and he, so to speak, fell on my neck like the father of the Prodigal Son. He hadna seen a Scotch face for four years. He raked up one or two high priests and gave instructions, and soon I was comfortably lodged in a part of the temple close to his own rooms. Eh, man, it was a noble sight to see Johnston and the priests. He was a big, red-haired fellow, six feet four, and as strong as a stot, with a voice like a north-easter, and yon natives fair crawled like caterpillars in his presence. I never saw a man with such a natural talent for being a god. You would have thought he had been bred to the job all his days, and yet I minded him keeping a grocer's shop in the Dalmarnock Road.

"That night he told me his story. It seemed that he had got a post at Shanghai in a trading house, and was coming out to it in one of those God-forgotten German tramps that defile the China seas. Like me, he fell in with a hurricane, and, like me, his

ship was doomed. He was a powerful swimmer, and managed to keep afloat until he found some drifting wreckage, and after the wind had gone down he paddled ashore. There he was captured by the savages, and taken, like me, to their city. They were going to sacrifice him, but one chief, wiser than the rest, called attention to his size and strength, and pointed out that they were at war with their neighbours, and that a big man would be of more use in the fighting line than on an altar in the temple.

"So off went Johnston to the wars. He was a bonny fighter, and very soon they made him captain of the royal bodyguard, and a fortnight later the general commanding-in-chief over the whole army. He said he had never enjoyed himself so much in his life, and when he got back from his battles the whole population of the city used to meet him with songs and flowers. Then an old priest found an ancient prophecy about a Red God who would come out of the sea and lead the people to victory. Very soon there was a strong party for making Johnston a god, and, when with the help of a few sticks of trade dynamite he had blown up the capital of the other side and brought back his army in triumph with a prisoner apiece, popular feeling could not be restrained. Johnston was hailed as divine. He hadna much grip of the language, and couldna explain the situation, so he thought it best to submit.

"'Mind you,' he said to me, 'I've been a good god to these poor blind ignorant folk.' He had stopped the worst of their habits and put down human sacrifices, and got a sort of town council appointed to keep the city clean, and he had made the army the most efficient thing ever heard of in the islands. And now he was preparing to leave. This was what they expected, for the prophecy had said that the Red God, after being the saviour of his people, would depart as he had come across the sea. So, under his directions, they had built him a kind of boat with which he hoped to reach Singapore. He had got together a considerable fortune, too, chiefly in rubies, for as a god he had plenty of opportunities of acquiring wealth honestly. He said there was a sort of greengrocer's and butcher's shop before his altar every morning, and he got one of the priests, who had some business notions, to sell off the goods for him.

"There was just one thing that bothered Mr. Johnston. He was a good Christian man and had been an elder in a kirk in the Cowcaddens, and he was much in doubt whether he had not committed a mortal sin in accepting the worship of these heathen islanders. Often I argued it out with him, but I did not seem able to comfort him rightly. 'Ye see,' he used to say to me, 'if I have broken anything, it's the spirit and no' the letter of the Commandment. I havena set up a graven image, for ye canna call me a graven image.'

"I mind that I quoted to him the conduct of Naaman, who was allowed to bow in the house of Rimmon, but he would not have it. 'No, no,' he cried, 'that has nothing to do with the point. It's no a question of my bowing in the house of Rimmon. I'm auld Rimmon himself."

□   □   □   □

"That's a strange story, Mr. Thomson," I said. "Is it true?"

"True as death. But you havena heard the end of it. We got away, and by and by we reached Singapore, and in course of time our native land. Johnston, he was a very rich man now, and I didna go without my portion; so the loss of the *Archibald McKelvie* turned out the best piece of luck in my life. I bought a share in Brock's Line, but nothing would content Johnston but that he must be a gentleman. He got a big estate in Annandale, where all the Johnstons came from long ago, and one way and another he has spent an awful siller on it. Land will swallow up money quicker than the sea."

"And what about his conscience?" I asked.

"It's keeping quieter," said Mr. Thomson. "He takes a great interest in Foreign Missions, to which he subscribes largely, and they tell me that he has given the funds to build several new kirks. Oh yes, and he's just been adopted as a prospective Liberal candidate. I had a letter from him no further back than yesterday. It's about his political career, as he calls it. He told me, what didna need telling, that I must never mention a word about his past. 'If discretion was necessary before,' he says, 'it's far more necessary now, for how could the Party of Progress have any confidence in a man if they heard he had once been a god?'"

Mr. PORTER'S INTENTIONS
By J. E. Buckrose

Drawings by
J. H. Hartley

"THERE'S Mr. Porter saying Good-bye again. Surely he's been walking out long enough," remarked Mathilda, as she peered with one eye through a clear ivy leaf in the ground-glass panel of Miss Simpson's door. "It's about time he walked *in*, if he's ever going to."

Having thus voiced in a nutshell the opinion of East Burnaby, she detached her eye from the ivy leaf, threw open the door, and appeared in the aperture with the expression of a demure white rabbit.

"Have the letters come yet?" fluttered her mistress, waving a neatly gloved hand in the direction of the disappointing Mr. Porter. She was greatly agitated.

"Not yet, 'm. Should I run down the lane and meet the postman?" asked Mathilda obligingly, for the postman was a personal friend.

"Don't trouble," replied Miss Simpson with feigned indifference—very badly feigned—"I'll just do a little gardening."

Gardening! In her new grey! And her best white hat! Mathilda knew at once that there was something behind it and went reluctantly indoors while Miss Simpson strolled to the mignonette bed, pulled up one weed very gingerly to satisfy her conscience, then stood by the gate to wait until the postman came up. Her hands shook, her knees trembled, she had an indescribable, sinking sensation beneath her waistbelt.

"Is there—" said the postman, glancing at a letter in his hand—"is there a Mr. E. N. Vandeleur here?"

"No!" palpitated Miss Simpson, and the postman began to put the letter back in his bag. "That is—yes——" she added, seizing the envelope from him and hastening with it towards the house.

"Rum!" meditated the postman. "Wonder who Mr. Vandeleur is—mebbe a sweetheart?" Then he suddenly began to chuckle: "Lor', what a joke it would be if some chap did come and cut out old Porter, what's been hangin' round and afraid to give

30

hisself away too cheap for the last five year!" So, still chuckling, he vanished round the corner of the road.

Miss Simpson, meanwhile, rushed by Mathilda up the stairs, unlocked the attic door, and shut it again with a nervous bang as if afraid lest any one should follow her in. The tea was overdrawn, the muffin spoiled, and the maid in a frenzy of balked curiosity, when her mistress came down with a burning spot on either cheek and an abstracted gaze which permitted a crack in the glass sugar basin to go unnoticed.

This, Mathilda felt, must indeed mean something serious.

Later that night the postman in his private capacity prowled round to the back-kitchen door. He bore in his hand a gift of lettuce for Miss Simpson in case of a surprise sortie. She considered him a model of correct behaviour, and so generous with his salads, poor young fellow.

"What's the chap like as you've got staying with you?" he asked in a whisper. "Fine joke if Miss Simpson was to take up with him and give old Porter the go-by."

"Chap—staying with us!" exclaimed his lady-love, goggling at him with her round eyes. "You must be going barmy, George." And she added, "You'd be none the worse for a bit of old Porter's back'ardness yourself."

"Well," responded the postman, "all I know is, I says to her, 'Have you got Mr. ——' I can't remember his name—'stopping here?' and she says, 'No—that is, yes—' just like that." He gave an impersonation of Miss Simpson in a hushed falsetto. "She didn't seem rightly sure whether she had or she hadn't, but she took the letter in, so he must be comed or coming. Well—so long!"

Mathilda closed the back door very gently, paused before a little glass to smooth her hair, and looked the sleekest of sleek bunnies as she went in with her mistress's cocoa. But Miss Simpson was not there; neither was she in any part of the house—or garden— and it was after ten o'clock. Mathilda listened. The house was quite silent. Then she heard the sound of a door being cautiously unlocked, a stealthy footfall on the attic stairs, and the meaning of it all flashed across her with such overwhelming conviction that the tray fell from her hands. He—the mysterious owner of the letter—was concealed up there!

It gave her a delicious thrill of terror and

excitement—like reading her favourite work, *Blood behind the Beam*, only more so.   And when Miss Simpson walked down towards her like a woman in a dream, cheeks crimson and shining eyes—she *knew*.

Next morning the farmer's wife came across early with the milk from the farm opposite, and the very birds seemed to be listening, as the two women chattered together in the dewy freshness near the lilac bush.   By tea-time, there was hardly a person in East Burnaby who did not know that Miss Simpson had a man hidden in her attic.

Thus blank and awful was the tale ; and Mrs. Poulton at the Grange led a certain section of public opinion when she charitably surmised that the stow-away was some poor ragged relation whom Miss Simpson was keeping out of the way until his wardrobe could be replenished ; the Vicar's wife *hoped* it might be an escaped convict ; but Mr. Porter, with the insight of awakened jealousy, felt sure it was a lover.

As he marched down the lane to Miss Simpson's, he saw the neat house, the neater income, and the woman he really liked, disappearing into the limbo of lost opportunities, and he said words to the nettles by the roadside which the nettles of East Burnaby were not in the habit of hearing.

"Miss Simpson *is* at home," he said fiercely, stalking into the drawing-room, where he tweaked the top off an india-rubber plant in his agitation.

"Mr. Porter !" said his hostess, coming upon him thus employed.

"What," answered John Porter, throwing the leaves into the fire-grate without apology, "is an indiarubber plant more or less to a ruined life ?"

Miss Simpson sat down suddenly.   She went very white.

"W—what on earth do you mean ?" she stammered faintly.

"What do I mean ?   I mean that you've played with me—toyed with my feelings—thrown me aside like an apple paring.   And for whom ?   For a man you have to keep locked up in your attic !"

Miss Simpson, though still faint, rose and edged towards the bell.

"A man—in my attic !" she echoed.

Mr. Porter ran round her with incredible agility and placed himself before the door.   "Don't try to take me in with any tales about convicts, or poor relations, or what not," he shouted.   "You've got a lover concealed up there !   You actually took in a letter for him five minutes after we parted yesterday.   Shame ! shame ! "

THE QUEEN'S
GIFT BOOK

WOMAN.

Hers the conflict, hers the conquest, hers the flag of life unfurl'd,
Hers the sorrow, hers the suffering, hers the love that rules the world.

From a painting by W. Hatherell, R.I.

He was beside himself with mortification. To think that he should have been outwitted thus! To think that any woman, after having had 'attention' paid her by him for a matter of five years or so, should dare to know another man existed.

"You own to taking in a letter addressed to some man here, don't you?"

"Yes, I took one in," gasped Miss Simpson.

"And you keep the attic locked?"

"Yes," again faltered Miss Simpson.

A blank silence followed, which Mr. Porter broke by a groan.

"I never knew how much I cared, Lætitia, until this happened," he said; and really he was thinking more of her than of the income or the neat house. Her companionship had grown into his selfish life more than he had ever realised.

An odd look came into Miss Simpson's face, and she sat for a little while twisting and untwisting her fingers; at last she got up from her chair and walked towards the door.

"May I trouble you to step upstairs?" she asked, in a low voice.

He gaped at her in miserable astonishment.

"You can't expect me to meet the feller!"

Miss Simpson seemed to grow.

"I demand it," she said.

So Mr. Porter stumped heavily after her, almost brushing against Mathilda, who lurked in ambush behind a curtain, and Miss Simpson waited for him with her hand upon the key of the attic door. They stood outside for a second's breathless pause.

"Now!" cried Miss Simpson, flinging open the door, and facing him, "there's Mr. E. N. Vandeleur!"

Mr. Porter glared round the empty room.

"Wha'—what?" he stammered. "I don't understand."

"I write last lines for competitions. I won five shillings under a nom-de-plume. I've made this my study because genius always does best in an attic."

Her tone was magnificent, but it dropped suddenly. "I ought to have put 'care of Miss Simpson.' I see that now."

"Can't you—can't you put it 'care of Mr. Porter,' for the rest of your life, Lætitia?" said he.

"Oh, John!" wept Miss Simpson.

And Mathilda scuttled from behind her curtain with round eyes staring and sharp ears pricked, for she had caught the distant, unmistakable sound of a kiss in the attic.

4

WOMAN
By Hall Caine

Painting by
W. Hatherell, R.I.

Then battle is in the blood of man, and the heroic part falls to him by right, but it is not in the blood of woman, who shrinks from it and loathes it, and yet, such is her nature, the fine and subtle mystery of it, that she flies to the scene of suffering with a bravery which far out-strips that of the man-at-arms. On the breasts that have borne tens of thousands of the sons who have fallen in this war the Red Cross is now enshrined. It is the new Scarlet Letter— the badge not of shame, but glory.—The Drama of 365 Days.

WHEN the Lord of the Creation gave the Woman to the Man,
In that blest but brief existence ere the rule of ill began,
Then He willed it that, if sharing in man's fault and in his fate,
She should therefore be his equal and the partner in his state.

Not to govern or cajole him, not to court or speak him smooth;
Not to snare or to enslave him, but to cheer, inspire, and soothe;
Not his temptress, not his slave-mate, not his subject, nor his squaw,
But his helpmeet and his angel by the right of God's own law.

If He cursed the Man with labour as the human lot's alloy,
He provided that for Woman his work should be his joy,
If He dowered the Man with passions which the grosser instincts move,
He reserved it to the Woman to uplift his lust to love.

If He ordered that the mother for the children of her womb
Should dare her death by travail and fight till crack of doom,
He ordained that by that impulse, still the purest and the best,
She should gather all that suffer in her pity to her breast.

Nurturing, nursing, guarding, guiding, giving strength with heart and
    hand,
Paying toll in pangs to Nature, which no man may understand,
Dauntless from the God who made her without fear to draw her breath,
Saviour of the weak and helpless, first at birth and last at death.

Since, the Lord creating Woman, she became a living soul,
Hers has been the old Earth's burthen, age on age, from pole to pole,
Hers the conflict, hers the conquest, hers the flag of life unfurl'd,
Hers the sorrow, hers the suffering, hers the love that rules the world.

THE HEROIC AGE
By Joseph Conrad

Painting by
C. M. Padday, R.O.I

October 1805

Drawings by
J. H. Hartley

"A FELLOW has now no chance of promotion unless he jumps into the muzzle of a gun and crawls out of the touch-hole."

He who, a hundred years ago, more or less, pronounced the above words in the uneasiness of his heart, thirsting for professional distinction, was a young naval officer.

Of his life, career, achievements, and end nothing is preserved for the edification of his young successors in the fleet of to-day—nothing but this phrase, which, sailor-like in the simplicity of personal sentiment and strength of graphic expression, embodies the spirit of the epoch. This obscure but vigorous testimony has its price, its significance, and its lesson. It comes to us from a worthy ancestor.

He belongs to the great array of the unknown—who are great, indeed, by the sum-total of the devoted effort put out, and the colossal scale of success attained by their insatiable and steadfast ambition. We do not know his name; we only know of him what is material for us to know—that he was never backward on occasions of desperate service. We have this on the authority of a distinguished seaman of Nelson's time.

Departing this life as Admiral of the Fleet on the eve of the Crimean War, Sir Thomas Byam Martin has recorded for us amongst his autobiographical notes these few characteristic words uttered by one young man of the many who must have felt that particular inconvenience of a heroic age.

The distinguished Admiral had lived through it himself, and was a good judge of what was expected in those days from men and ships. A brilliant frigate captain, a man of sound judgment, of dashing bravery and of serene mind, scrupulously concerned for the welfare and honour of the navy, he missed a larger fame only by the chances of the service.

We may well quote on this day the words written of Nelson, in the decline of a well-spent life, by Sir T. B. Martin, who died seventy years ago on the very anniversary of Trafalgar.

" Nelson's nobleness of mind was a prominent and beautiful part of his character. His foibles—faults if you like—will never be dwelt upon in any memorandum of mine," he declares, and goes on : " He whose splendid and matchless achievements will be remembered with admiration while there is gratitude in the hearts of Britons, or while a ship floats upon the ocean ; he whose example on the breaking out of the war gave so chivalrous an impulse to the younger men of the service that all rushed into rivalry of daring which disdained every warning of prudence, and led to acts of heroic enterprise which tended greatly to exalt the glory of our nation."

" Exalt," he wrote, not " augment." And therein his feelings and his pen captured the very truth. Other men there were ready and able to add to the treasure of victories the British navy has given to the nation. It was the lot of Lord Nelson to exalt all this glory. Exalt ! The word seems to be created for the man.

□　　　□　　　□　　　□

The British navy is rich in victories beyond the wildest dreams of success and fame.

It may well, on culminating days of its history, cast about for the memory of some reverses to appease the jealous fates which attend the prosperity and triumphs of a nation. It holds, indeed, the heaviest inheritance that has ever been entrusted to the courage and fidelity of armed men.

In all the records of history there has never been a time when a victorious fortune has been so faithful to men making war upon the sea. And it must be confessed that on their part they knew how to be faithful to their victorious Fortune. They were exalted. They were always watching for her smile ; night or day, fair weather or foul, they waited for her slightest sign with the offering of their stout hearts in their hands. And for the inspiration of this high constancy they were indebted to Lord Nelson alone. Whatever earthly affection he abandoned or grasped, the great Admiral was always, before all, beyond all, a lover of Fame. He loved her jealously, with an inextinguishable ardour and an insatiable desire—he loved her with a masterful devotion and an infinite trustfulness. He was a flaming example to the wooers of glorious fortune.

There have been great officers before—Lord Hood, for instance, whom he himself regarded as the greatest sea officer England ever had. A long succession of great commanders opened the sea to the vast range of Nelson's genius. His time had come ; and, after the

THE HEROIC AGE.

Lord Nelson appears to us as the first of the moderns.

From a painting by C. M. Padday, R.I.

THE QUEEN'S
GIFT BOOK

great sea officers, the great naval tradition passed into the keeping of a great man. In a few short years he revolutionised, not the strategy or tactics of sea-warfare, but the very conception of victory itself. And this is genius. In that alone, through the fidelity of his fortune and the power of his inspiration, he stands unique amongst the leaders of fleets and sailors. He brought heroism into the line of duty. Verily he is a terrible ancestor.

And the men of his day loved him. They loved him not only as victorious armies have loved great commanders; they loved him with a more intimate feeling as one of themselves. To be so great and to remain so accessible to the affection of one's fellow-men is the mark of exceptional humanity. Lord Nelson's greatness was very human. It had a moral basis; it needed to feel itself surrounded by the warm devotion of a band of brothers. He was a seaman of seamen. Sir T. B. Martin states that he never conversed with any officer who had served under Nelson "without hearing the heartiest expressions of attachment to his person and admiration of his frank and conciliatory manner to his subordinates." And Sir Robert Stopford, who commanded one of the ships with which Nelson chased to the West Indies a fleet nearly double in number, says in a letter: "We are half-starved and otherwise inconvenienced by being so long out of port, but our reward is that we are with Nelson."

This heroic spirit of daring and endurance, in which all public and private differences were sunk throughout the whole fleet, is Lord Nelson's great legacy, triply sealed by the victorious impress of the Nile, Copenhagen, and Trafalgar. This is a legacy whose value the changes of time cannot affect. The men and the ships he knew how to lead lovingly to the work of courage and the reward of glory have passed away, but Nelson's uplifting touch remains in the standard of achievement he has set for all time. It must not be forgotten that this was the first time when Nelson, commanding in chief, had his opponents under way—the first time and the last. Had he lived, had there been other fleets left to oppose him, we should, perhaps, have learned something more of his greatness as a sea officer. Nothing could have been added to his greatness as a leader. All that can be affirmed is, that on no other day of his short and glorious career was Lord Nelson more splendidly true to his genius and to his country's fortune.

□   □   □   □

The modern naval man must feel that the time has come for the tactical practice of the great sea officers of the past to be laid by in the temple of august memories. The fleet tactics of the sailing days were governed by two points: the deadly nature of a raking fire,

and the dread, natural to a commander dependent upon the winds, of finding at some crucial moment part of his fleet thrown hopelessly to leeward. These two points were of the very essence of sailing tactics, and these two points have been eliminated from the modern tactical problem by the changes of propulsion and armament. Lord Nelson was the first to disregard them with conviction and audacity

sustained by an unbounded trust in the men he led. This conviction, this audacity, and this trust stand out from amongst the lines of the celebrated memorandum, which is but a declaration of his faith in a crushing superiority of fire as the only means of victory and the only aim of sound tactics. Under the difficulties of the then existing conditions he strove for that, and for that alone, putting his faith into practice against every risk. And in that exclusive faith Lord Nelson appears to us as the first of the moderns.

Against every risk, I have said; and the men of to-day, born and bred to the use of steam, can hardly realise how much of that risk was in the weather. Except at the Nile, where the conditions were ideal for engaging a fleet moored in shallow water, Lord Nelson was not lucky in his weather. Practically it was nothing but a quite unusual failure of the wind which cost him his arm during the Teneriffe expedition. On Trafalgar Day the weather was not so much unfavourable as extremely dangerous.

It was one of those covered days of fitful sunshine, of light, unsteady winds, with a swell from the westward, and hazy in general, but with the land about the Cape at times distinctly visible. My experience has convinced me that, in that corner of the ocean, once the wind has got to the northward of west (as it did on the 20th, taking the British fleet aback), appearances of westerly weather go for nothing, and that it is infinitely more likely to veer right round to the east than to shift back again. It was in those conditions that, at seven on the morning of the 21st, the signal for the fleet to bear up and steer east was made. Holding a clear recollection of these languid easterly sighs rippling unexpectedly against the run of the smooth swell, with no other warning than a ten-minutes' calm and a queer darkening of the coast-line, I cannot think without a gasp of professional awe of that fateful moment. To this day I cannot free myself from the impression that, for some forty minutes, the fate of the great battle hung upon a breath of wind such as I have felt stealing from behind, as it were, upon my cheek while engaged in looking to the westward for the signs of the weather.

Never more shall British seamen going into action have to trust the success of their valour to a breath of wind. The God of gales and

battles, favouring her arms to the last, has let the sun of England's sailing-fleet and of its greatest master set in unclouded glory. And now that the old ships and their men are gone, the new ships and the new men, many of them bearing the old, auspicious names, have taken up their watch on the stern and impartial sea, which offers no opportunities but to those who know how to grasp them with a ready hand and an undaunted heart.

□　　　□　　　□　　　□

This the navy of the Twenty Years' War knew well how to do, and never better than when Lord Nelson had breathed into its soul his own passion for honour and fame. It was a fortunate navy. Its victories were no mere smashing of helpless ships and massacres of cowed men. It was spared that cruel favour, for which no brave heart had ever prayed. It was fortunate in its adversaries. I say adversaries, for on recalling such proud memories we should avoid the word "enemies," whose hostile sound perpetuates the antagonisms and strife of nations, so irremediable perhaps, so fateful—and also so vain.

One of them disorganised by revolutionary changes, the other rusted in the neglect of a decayed monarchy, the two fleets opposed to us entered the contest with odds against them from the first. By the merit of our daring and our faithfulness, and the genius of a great leader, we augmented our advantage during the course of the war and kept it to the last. But in the exulting illusion of irresistible might a long series of military successes brings to a nation, the less obvious aspect of such a fortune may perchance be lost to view. The old navy in its last days earned a fame that no belittling malevolence dare cavil at. And this supreme favour they owe to their adversaries alone.

Deprived by an ill-starred fortune of that self-confidence which strengthens the hands of an armed host, impaired in skill but not in courage, it may safely be said that our adversaries managed yet to make a better fight of it in 1797 than they did in 1793.

Later still, the resistance offered at the Nile was all that could be demanded from seamen, who, unless blind or without understanding, must have seen their doom sealed from the moment that the *Goliath*, bearing up under the bows of the *Guerrier*, took up an inshore berth.

The combined fleets of 1805, just come out of port, and attended by nothing but the disturbing memories of reverses, presented to our approach a determined front, on which Captain Blackwood, in a knightly spirit, congratulated his Admiral. By the exertions of their valour our adversaries have but added a greater lustre to our arms. No friend could have done more; for even in war, which severs for a time all the sentiments of human fellowship, this subtle bond of association remains between brave men—that the final testimony to the value of victory must be received at the hands of the vanquished.

Those who from the heat of that battle sank together to their repose in the cool depths of the ocean would not understand the watchwords of our day, would gaze with amazed eyes at the engines of our strife.

All passes, all changes: the animosity of peoples, the handling of fleets, the forms of ships, and even the sea itself seems to wear a different and diminished aspect from the sea of Lord Nelson's day.

In this ceaseless rush of shadows and shades, that, like the fantastic forms of clouds cast darkly upon the waters, fly past us to fall headlong below the hard edge of an implacable horizon, we must turn to the national spirit, which, superior in its force and continuity to good and evil fortune, can alone give us the feeling of an enduring existence and of an invincible power against the fates.

Like a subtle and mysterious elixir poured into the perishable clay of successive generations, it grows in truth, splendour, and potency with the march of ages. In its incorruptible flow all round the globe of the earth it preserves from the decay and forget-fulness of death the greatness of our great men, and amongst them the passionate and gentle greatness of Lord Nelson, the nature of whose genius was, on the testimony of a brave seaman and distinguished Admiral, such as to " Exalt the glory of our nation."

THE MAGIC CIRCLE
By Ethel M. Dell
Painting by
W. Russell Flint, A.R.W.S.
Drawings by E. H. Shepard

THE persistent chirping of a sparrow made it almost harder to bear. Lady Brooke rose abruptly from the table, her black brows drawn close together, and swept to the window to scare the intruder away.

" I really have not the smallest idea what your objections can be," she observed, pausing with her back to the room.

" A little exercise of your imagination might be of some assistance to you," returned her husband drily, not troubling to raise his eyes from his paper.

He was leaning back in a chair in an attitude of unstudied ease. It was characteristic of Sir Roland Brooke to make himself physically comfortable at least, whatever his mental atmosphere. He seldom raised his voice, and never swore. Yet there was about him a certain amount of force that made itself felt more by his silence than his speech.

His young wife, though she shrugged her shoulders and looked contemptuous, did not venture upon open defiance.

" I am to decline the invitation, then ? " she asked presently, without turning.

" Certainly ! " Sir Roland again made leisurely reply as he scanned the page before him.

" And give as an excuse that you are too staunch a Tory to approve of such an innovation as the waltz ? "

" You may give any excuse that you consider suitable," he returned with unruffled composure.

" I know of none," she answered, with a quick vehemence that trembled on the edge of rebellion.

Sir Roland turned very slowly in his chair and regarded the delicate outline of his wife's figure against the window-frame.

" Then, my dear," he said very deliberately, " let me recommend you once more to have recourse to your ever romantic imagination."

She quivered, and clenched her hands, as if goaded beyond endurance. " You do not treat me fairly," she murmured under her breath.

Sir Roland continued to look at her with the air of a naturalist examining an interesting specimen of his cult. He said nothing till, driven by his scrutiny, she turned and faced him.

" What is your complaint ? " he asked then.

41

She hesitated for an instant. There was doubt—even a hint of fear—upon her beautiful face. Then, with a certain recklessness, she spoke :

"I have been accustomed to freedom of action all my life. I never dreamed, when I married you, that I should be called upon to sacrifice this."

Her voice quivered. She would not meet his eyes. Sir Roland sat and passively regarded her. His face expressed no more than a detached and waning interest.

"I am sorry," he said finally, "that the romance of your marriage has ceased to attract you. But I was not aware that its hold upon you was ever very strong."

Lady Brooke made a quick movement, and broke into a light laugh.

"It certainly did not fall upon very fruitful ground," she said. "It is scarcely surprising that it did not flourish."

Sir Roland made no response. The interest had faded entirely from his face. He looked supremely bored.

Lady Brooke moved towards the door.

"It seems to be your pleasure to thwart me at every turn," she said. "A labourer's wife has more variety in her existence than I."

"Infinitely more," said Sir Roland, returning to his paper. "A labourer's wife, my dear, has an occasional beating to chasten her spirit, and she is considerably the better for it."

His wife stood still, very erect and queenly.

"Not only the better, but the happier," she said very bitterly. "Even a dog would rather be beaten than kicked to one side."

Sir Roland lowered his paper again with startling suddenness.

"Is that your point of view ? " he said. "Then I fear I have been neglecting my duty most outrageously. However, it is an omission easily remedied. Let me hear no more of this masquerade, Lady Brooke ! You have my orders, and if you transgress them you will be punished in a fashion scarcely to your liking. Is that clearly understood ? "

He looked straight up at her with cold, smiling eyes that yet seemed to convey a steely warning.

She shivered very slightly as she encountered them. "You make a mockery of everything," she said, her voice very low.

Sir Roland uttered a quiet laugh.

"I am, nevertheless, a man of my word, Naomi," he said. "If you wish to test me, you have your opportunity."

He immersed himself finally in his paper as he ended, and she, with a smile of proud contempt, turned and passed from the room.

She had married him out of pique, it was true, but life with him had never seemed intolerable until he had shown her that he knew it.

□   □   □   □

She took her invitation with her, and in her own room sat down to read it once again. It was from a near neighbour, Lady Blythebury, an acquaintance with whom she was more intimate than was Sir Roland. Lady Blythebury was a very lively person indeed. She had been on the stage in her young days, and she had decidedly advanced ideas on the subject of social entertainment. As a hostess, she was notorious for her originality and energy, and, though some of the county families disapproved of her, she always knew how to secure as many guests as she desired. Lady Brooke had known her previous to her own marriage, and she clung to this friendship, notwithstanding Sir Roland's very obvious lack of sympathy.

He knew Lord Blythebury in the hunting-field. Their properties adjoined, and it was inevitable that certain courtesies should be exchanged. But he refused so steadily to fall a captive to Lady Blythebury's bow and spear, that he very speedily aroused her aversion. He soon realised that her influence over his wife was very far from benevolent towards himself, but, save that he persisted in declining all social invitations to Blythebury, he made no attempt to counteract the evil. In fact, it was not his custom to coerce her. He denied her very little, though with regard to that little he was as adamant.

But to Naomi his non-interference was many a time more galling than his interdiction. It was but seldom that she attempted to oppose him, and, save that Lady Blythebury's masquerade had been discussed between them for weeks, she would not have greatly cared for his refusal to attend it. When Sir Roland asserted himself, it was her habit to yield without argument.

But now, for the first time, she asked herself if he were not presuming upon her wifely submission. He would think more of her if she resisted him, whispered her hurt pride, recalling the courteous indifference which it was his custom to mete out to her. But dared she do this thing ?

She took up the invitation again and read it. It was to be a fancy dress ball, and all were to wear masks. The waltz, which she had learned to dance from Lady Blythebury herself and which was only just coming into vogue in England, was to be one of the great features of the evening. There would be no foolish formality, Lady Blythebury had assured her. The masks would preclude that. Altogether the whole entertainment promised to be of so entrancing a nature that she had permitted herself to look forward to it with considerable pleasure. But she might have guessed that Sir Roland would refuse to go, she reflected, as she sat in her dainty room with the invitation before her. Did he ever attend any function that was not so stiff and dull that she invariably pined to depart from the moment of arrival ?

Again she read the invitation, recalling Lady Blythebury's gay words when last they had talked the matter over.

" If only Una could come without the lion for once ! " she had said.

And she herself had almost echoed the wish. Sir Roland always spoilt everything.

Well !——She took up her pen. She supposed she must refuse. A moment it hovered above the paper. Then, very slowly, it descended and began to write.

□   □   □

The chatter of many voices and the rhythm of dancing feet, the strains of a string-band in the distance, and, piercing all, the clear, high notes of a flute, filled the spring night with wonderful sound. Lady Blythebury had turned her husband's house into a fairy palace of delight. She stood in the doorway of the ballroom, her florid face beaming above her Elizabethan ruffles, looking in upon the gay and ever-shifting scene which she had called into being.

" I feel as if I had stepped into an Arabian Night," she laughed to one of her guests, who stood beside her. He was dressed as a court jester, and carried a wand which he flourished dramatically. He wore a close-fitting black mask.

" There is certainly magic abroad," he declared, in a rich, Irish brogue that Lady Blythebury smiled to hear. For she also was Irish to the backbone.

" You know something of the art yourself, Captain Sullivan ? " she asked.

She knew the man for a friend of her husband's. He was more or less disreputable, she believed, but he was none the less welcome on that account. It was just such men as he who knew how to make things a success. She relied upon the disreputable more than she would have admitted.

" Egad, I'm no novice in most things ! " declared the court jester, waving his wand bombastically. " But it's the magic of a pretty woman that I'm after at the present moment. These masks, Lady Blythebury, are uncommon inconvenient. It's yourself that knows better than to wear one. Sure, beauty should never go veiled."

Lady Blythebury laughed indulgently. Though she knew it for what it was, the fellow's blarney was good to hear.

" Ah, go and dance ! " she said. " I've heard all that before. It never means anything. Go and dance with the little lady over there in the pink domino ! I give you my word that she is pretty. Her name is Una, but she is minus the lion on this occasion. I shall tell you no more than that."

THE MAGIC CIRCLE.

Darting past him like a frightened bird.

From a painting by W. Russell Flint, A.R.W.S.

THE QUEEN'S
GIFT BOOK

"Egad! It's more than enough!" said the court jester, as he bowed and moved away.

The lady indicated stood alone in the curtained embrasure of a bay window. She was watching the dancers with an absorbed air, and did not notice his approach.

He drew near, walking with a free swagger in time to the haunting waltz-music. Reaching her, he stopped and executed a sweeping bow, his hand upon his heart.

"May I have the pleasure——"

She looked up with a start. Her eyes shone through her mask with a momentary irresolution as she bent in response to his bow.

With scarcely a pause he offered her his arm.

"You dance the waltz?"

She hesitated for a second; then, with an affirmatory murmur, accepted the proffered arm. The bold stare with which he met her look had in it something of compulsion.

He led her instantly away from her retreat, and in a moment his hand was upon her waist. He guided her into the gay stream of dancers without a word.

They began to waltz—a dream-waltz in which she seemed to float without effort, without conscious volition. Instinctively she responded to his touch, keenly, vibrantly aware of the arm that supported her, of the dark, free eyes that persistently sought her own.

"Faith!" he suddenly said in his soft, Irish voice. "To find Una without the lion is a piece of good fortune I had scarcely prayed for. And what was the persuasion that you used at all to keep the monster in his den?"

She glanced up, half startled by his speech. What did this man know about her?

"If you mean my husband," she said at last, "I did not persuade him. He never wished or intended to come."

Her companion laughed as one well pleased.

"Very generous of him!" he commented, in a tone that sent the blood to her cheeks.

He guided her dexterously among the dancers. The girl's breath came quickly, unevenly, but her feet never faltered.

"If I were the lion," said her partner daringly, "by the powers, I'd play the part! I wouldn't be a tame beast, egad! If Una went out to a fancy ball, my faith, I would go too!"

Lady Brooke uttered a little, excited laugh. The words caught her interest.

" And suppose Una went without your leave ? " she said.

The Irishman looked at her with a humorous twist at one corner of his mouth.

" I'm thinking that I'd still go too," he said.

" But if you didn't know ? " She asked the question with a curious vehemence. Her instinct told her that, however he might profess to trifle, here at least was a man.

" That wouldn't happen," he said, with conviction, " if I were the lion."

The music was quickening to the *finale*, and she felt the strong arm grow tense about her.

" Come ! " he said. " We will go into the garden."

She went with him because it seemed that she must, but deep in her heart there lurked a certain misgiving. There was an almost arrogant air of power about this man. She wondered what Sir Roland would say if he knew, and comforted herself almost immediately with the reflection that he never could know. He had gone to Scotland, and she did not expect him back for several weeks.

So she turned aside with this stranger, and passed out upon his arm into the dusk of the soft spring night.

" You know these gardens well ? " he questioned.

She came out of her meditations.

" Not really well. Lady Blythebury and I are friends, but we do not visit very often."

" And that but secretly," he laughed, " when the lion is absent ? " She did not answer him, and he continued after a moment : " 'Pon my life, the very mention of him seems to cast a cloud. Let us draw a magic circle, and exclude him ! " He waved his wand. " You knew that I was a magician ? "

There was a hint of something more than banter in his voice. They had reached the end of the terrace, and were slowly descending the steps. But at his last words, Lady Brooke stood suddenly still.

" I only believe in one sort of magic," she said, " and that is beyond the reach of all but fools."

Her voice quivered with an almost passionate disdain. She was suddenly aware of an intense, burning misery that seemed to gnaw into her very soul. Why had she come out with this buffoon ? she wondered. Why had she come to the masquerade at all ? She was utterly out of sympathy with its festive gaiety. A great and overmastering desire for solitude descended upon her. She turned almost angrily to go.

But in the same instant the jester's hand caught her own.

"Even so, lady," he said. "But the magic of fools has led to paradise before now."

She laughed out bitterly :

"A fool's paradise !"

"Is ever green," he said whimsically. "Faith, it's no place at all for cynics. Shall we go hand in hand to find it then—in case you miss the way ?"

She laughed again at the quaint adroitness of his speech. But her lips were curiously unsteady, and she found the darkness very comforting. There was no moon, and the sky was veiled. She suffered the strong clasp of his fingers about her own without protest. What did it matter—for just one night ?

"Where are we going ?" she asked.

"Wait till we get there !" murmured her companion. "We are just within the magic circle. Una has escaped from the lion."

She felt turf beneath her feet, and once or twice the brushing of twigs against her hand. She began to have a faint suspicion as to whither he was leading her. But she would not ask a second time. She had yielded to his guidance, and though her heart fluttered strangely she would not seem to doubt. The dread of Sir Roland's displeasure had receded to the back of her mind. Surely there was indeed magic abroad that night ! It seemed diffused in the very air she breathed. In silence they moved along the dim grass path. From far away there came to them fitfully the sound of music, remote and wonderful, like straying echoes of paradise. A soft wind stirred above them, lingering secretly among opening leaves. There was a scent of violets almost intoxicatingly sweet.

The silence seemed magnetic. It held them like a spell. Through it, vague and intangible as the night at first, but gradually taking definite shape, strange thoughts began to rise in the girl's heart.

She had consented to this adventure from sheer lack of purpose. But whither was it leading her ? She was a married woman, with her shackles heavy upon her. Yet she walked that night with a stranger, as one who owned her freedom. The silence between them was intimate and wonderful, the silence which only kindred spirits can ever know. It possessed her magically, making her past life seem dim and shadowy, and the present only real.

And yet she knew that she was not free. She trespassed on forbidden ground. She tasted the forbidden fruit, and found it tragically sweet.

Suddenly and softly he spoke :

"Does the magic begin to work ?"

She started and tried to stop. Surely it were wiser to go back while she had the will ! But he drew her forward still. The mist overhead was faintly silver. The moon was rising.

" We will go to the heart of the tangle," he said. " There is nothing to fear. The lion himself could not frighten you here."

Again she yielded to him. There was a suspicion of raillery in his voice that strangely reassured her. The grasp of his hand was very close.

" We are in the maze," she said at last, breaking her silence. " Are you sure of the way ? "

He answered her instantly with complete self-assurance.

" Like the heart of a woman, it's hard that it is to find. But I think I have the key. And if not, by the saints, I'm near enough now to break through."

The words thrilled her inexplicably. Truly the magic was swift and potent. A few more steps, and she was aware of a widening of the hedge. They were emerging into the centre of the maze.

" Ah," said the jester, " I thought I should win through ! "

He led her forward into the shadow of a great tree. The mist was passing very slowly from the sky. By the silvery light that filtered down from the hidden moon Naomi made out the strong outline of his shoulders as he stood before her, and the vague darkness of his mask.

She put up her free hand and removed her own. The breeze had died down. The atmosphere was hushed and airless.

" Do you know the way back ? " she asked him, in a voice that sounded unnatural even to herself.

" Do you want to go back, then ? " he queried keenly.

There was something in his tone—a subtle something that she had not detected before. She began to tremble. For the first time, actual fear took hold of her.

" You must know the way back ! " she exclaimed. " This is folly ! They will be wondering where we are."

" Faith, Lady Una ! It is the fool's paradise," he told her coolly. " They will not wonder. They know too well that there is no way back."

His manner terrified her. Its very quietness seemed a menace. Desperately she tore herself from his hold, and turned to escape. But it was as though she fled in a nightmare. Whichever way she turned, she met only the impenetrable ramparts of the hedge that surrounded her. She could find neither entrance nor exit. It was as though the way by which she had come had been closed behind her.

But the brightness above was growing. She whispered to herself that she would soon be able to see, that she could not be a prisoner for long.

Suddenly she heard her captor close to

her, and, turning in terror, she found him erect and dominating against the hedge. With a tremendous effort she controlled her rising panic to plead with him.

"Indeed, I must go back!" she said, her voice unsteady, but very urgent. "I have already stayed too long. You cannot wish to keep me here against my will?"

She saw him shrug his shoulders slightly.

"There is no way back," he said, "or, if there is, I do not know it."

There was no dismay in his voice, but neither was there exultation. He simply stated the fact with absolute composure. Her heart gave a wild throb of misgiving. Was the man wholly sane?

Again she caught wildly at her failing courage, and drew herself up to her full height. Perhaps she might awe him, even yet.

"Sir," she said, "I am Sir Roland Brooke's wife. And I——"

"Egad!" he broke in banteringly, "that was yesterday. You are free to-day. I have brought you out of bondage. We have found paradise together, and, my pretty Lady Una, there is no way back."

"But there is, there is!" she cried desperately. "And I must find it! I tell you I am Sir Roland Brooke's wife. I belong to him. No one can keep me from him!"

It was as though she beat upon an iron door.

"There is no way out of the magic circle," said the jester inexorably.

A white shaft of light illumined the mist above them, revealing the girl's pale face, making sinister the man's masked one. He seemed to be smiling. He bent towards her.

"You seem amazingly fond of your chains," he said softly. "And yet, from what I have heard, Sir Roland is no gentle tyrant. How is it, pretty one? What makes you cling to your bondage so?"

"He is my husband!" she said, through white lips.

"Faith, that is no answer," he declared. "Own, now, that you hate him, that you loathe his presence, and shudder at his touch! I told you I was a magician, Lady Una; but you wouldn't believe me at all."

She confronted him with a sudden fury that marvellously reinforced her failing courage.

"You lie, sir!" she cried, stamping passionately upon the soft earth. "I do none of these things. I have never hated him. I have never shrunk from his touch. We have not understood each other, perhaps, but that is a different matter, and no concern of yours."

"He has not made you happy," said the jester persistently. "You will never go back to him now that you are free!"

"I will go back to him!" she cried stormily. "How dare you say such a thing to me? How dare you?"

He came nearer to her.

5

"Listen!" he said. "It is deliverance that I am offering you. I ask nothing at all in return, simply to make you happy, and to teach you the blessed magic which now you scorn. Faith! It's the greatest game in the world, Lady Una; and it only takes two players, dear, only two players!"

There was a subtle, caressing quality in his voice. His masked face was bending close to hers. She felt trapped and helpless, but she forced herself to stand her ground.

"You insult me!" she said, her voice quivering, but striving to be calm.

"Never a bit!" he declared. "Since I am the truest friend you have!"

She drew away from him with a gesture of repulsion.

"You insult me!" she said again. "I have my husband, and I need no other."

He laughed sneeringly, the insinuating banter all gone from his manner.

"You know he is nothing to you," he said. "He neglects you. He bullies you. You married him because you wanted to be a married woman. Be honest, now! You never loved him. You do not know what love is!"

"It is false!" she cried. "I will not listen to you. Let me go!"

He took a sudden step forward.

"You refuse deliverance?" he questioned harshly.

She did not retreat this time, but faced him proudly.

"I do!"

"Listen!" he said again, and his voice was stern. "Sir Roland Brooke has returned home. He knows that you have disobeyed him. He knows that you are here with me. You will not dare to face him. You have gone too far to return."

She gasped hysterically, and tottered for an instant, but recovered herself.

"I will—I will go back!" she said.

"He will beat you like a labourer's wife," warned the jester. "He may do worse."

She was swaying as she stood.

"He will do—as he sees fit," she said.

He stooped a little lower.

"I would make you happy, Lady Una," he whispered. "I would protect you—shelter you—love you!"

She flung out her hands with a wild and desperate gesture. The magnetism of his presence had become horrible to her.

"I am going to him—now," she said.

Behind him she saw, in the brightening moonlight, the opening which she had vainly sought a few minutes before. She sprang for it, darting past him like a frightened bird seeking refuge, and in another moment she was lost in the green labyrinths.

□   □   □   □

The moonlight had become clear and strong, casting black shadows all about her. Twice, in her frantic efforts to escape, she ran back into the centre of the maze. The jester had gone, but she imagined him lurking behind every corner, and she impotently recalled his words : "There is no way out of the magic circle."

At last, panting and exhausted, she knew that she was unwinding the puzzle. Often as its intricacies baffled her, she kept her head, rectifying each mistake and pressing on, till the wider curve told her that she was very near the entrance. She came upon it finally quite suddenly, and found herself, to her astonishment, close to the terrace steps.

She mounted them with trembling limbs, and paused a moment to summon her composure. Then, outwardly calm, she traversed the terrace and entered the house.

Lady Blythebury was dancing, and she felt she could not wait. She scribbled a few hasty words of farewell, and gave them to a servant as she entered her carriage. Hers was the first departure, and no one noted it.

She sank back at length thankfully in the darkness, and closed her eyes. Whatever lay before her, she had escaped from the nightmare horror of the shadowy garden.

But as the brief drive neared its end, her anxiety revived. Had Sir Roland indeed returned and discovered her absence ? Was it possible ?

Her face was white and haggard as she entered the hall at last. Her eyes were hunted.

The servant who opened to her looked at her oddly for a moment.

"What is it ? " she said nervously.

"Sir Roland has returned, my lady," he said. "He arrived two hours ago, and went straight to his room, saying he would not disturb your ladyship."

She turned away in silence, and mounted the stairs. Did he know ? Had he guessed ? Was it that that had brought him back ?

She entered her room, and dismissed the maid she found awaiting her.

Swiftly she threw off the pink domino, and began to loosen her hair with stiff, fumbling fingers ; then shook it about her shoulders, and sank shivering upon a couch. She could not go to bed. The terror that possessed her was too intense, too overmastering.

Ah ! What was that ? Every pulse in her body leaped and stood still, at sound of a low

knock at the door. Who could it be? gasped her fainting heart.
Not Sir Roland surely? He never came to her room now.

Softly the door opened. It was Sir Roland and none other—Sir
Roland wearing an old velvet smoking-jacket, composed as ever, his
grey eyes very level and inscrutable.

He paused for a single instant upon the threshold, then came noiselessly in and closed the door.

Naomi sat motionless and speechless. She lacked the strength
to rise. Her hands were pressed upon her heart. She thought its
beating would suffocate her.

He came quietly across the room to her, not seeming to notice
her agitation.

"I should not have disturbed you at this hour if I had not been
sure that you were awake," he said.

Reaching her, he bent and touched her white cheek.

"Why, child, how cold you are!" he said.

She started violently back, and then, as a sudden memory assailed
her, she caught his hand and held it for an instant.

"It is nothing," she said with an effort. "You—you startled
me."

"You are nervous to-night," said Sir Roland.

She shrank under his look.

"You see, I did not expect you," she murmured.

"Evidently not." Sir Roland stood gravely considering her. "I
came back," he said, after a moment, "because it occurred to me
that you might be lonely after all, in spite of your assurance to the
contrary. I did not ask you to accompany me, Naomi. I did not
think you would care to do so. But I regretted it later, and I have
come back to remedy the omission. Will you come with me to Scotland?"

His tone was quiet and somewhat formal, but there was in it a
kindliness that sent the blood pulsing through her veins in a wave of
relief even greater than her astonishment at his words. He did not
know, then. That was her one all-possessing thought. He could not
know, or he had not spoken to her thus.

She sat slowly forward, drawing her hair about her shoulders like
a cloak. She felt for the moment an overpowering weakness, and
she could not look up.

"I will come, of course," she said at last, her voice very low, "if
you wish it."

Sir Roland did not respond at once. Then, as his silence was
beginning to disquiet her again, he laid a steady hand upon the shadow-
ing hair.

"My dear," he said gently, "have you no wishes upon the subject?"

Again she started at his touch, and again, as if to rectify the start, drew ever so slightly nearer to him. It was many, many days since she had heard that tone from him.

"My wishes are yours," she told him faintly.

His hand was caressing her softly, very softly. Again he was silent for a while, and into her heart there began to creep a new feeling that made her gradually forget the immensity of her relief. She sat motionless, save that her head drooped a little lower, ever a little lower.

"Naomi," he said, at last, "I have been thinking a good deal lately. We seem to have been wandering round and round in a circle. I have been wondering if we could not by any means find a way out?"

She made a sharp, involuntary movement. What was this that he was saying to her?

"I don't quite understand," she murmured.

His hand pressed a little upon her, and she knew that he was bending down.

"You are not happy," he said, with grave conviction.

She could not contradict him.

"It is my own fault," she managed to say, without lifting her head.

"I do not think so," he returned, "at least, not entirely. I know that there have frequently been times when you have regretted your marriage. For that you were not to blame." He paused an instant. "Naomi," he said, a new note in his voice, "I think I am right in believing that, notwithstanding this regret, you do not in your heart wish to leave me?"

She quivered, and hid her face in silence.

He waited a few seconds, and finally went on as if she had answered in the affirmative.

"That being so, I have a foundation on which to build. I would not ask of you anything which you feel unable to grant. But there is only one way for us to get out of the circle that I can see. Will you take it with me, Naomi? Shall we go away together, and leave this miserable estrangement behind us?"

His voice was low and tender. Yet she felt instinctively that he had not found it easy to expose his most sacred reserve thus. She moved convulsively, trying to answer him, trying for several unworthy moments to accept in silence the shelter his generosity had offered her. But her efforts failed, for she had not been moulded for deception; and this new weapon of his had cut her to the heart. Heavy, shaking sobs overcame her.

"Hush!" he said. "Hush! I never dreamed you felt it so."

"Ah, you don't know me!" she whispered. "I—I am not what you think me. I have disobeyed you, deceived you, cheated you!" Humbled to the earth, she made piteous, halting confession before her tyrant.

"I was at the masquerade to-night. I waltzed—and afterwards

went into the maze—in the dark—with a stranger—who made love to me. I—never—meant you—to know."

Silence succeeded her words, and, as she waited for him to rise and spurn her, she wondered how she had ever brought herself to utter them. But she would not have recalled them even then. He moved at last, but not as she had anticipated. He gathered the tumbled hair back from her face, and, bending over her, he spoke. Even in her agony of apprehension she noted the curious huskiness of his voice.

"And yet you told me," he said. "Why?"

She could not answer him, nor could she raise her face. He was not angry, she knew now; but yet she felt that she could not meet his eyes.

There was a short silence, then he spoke again, close to her ear:

"You need not have told me, Naomi."

The words amazed her. With a great start of bewilderment she lifted her head and looked at him. He put his hands upon her shoulders. She thought she saw a smile hovering about his lips, but it was of a species she had never seen there before.

"Because," he explained gently, "I knew."

She stared at him in wonder, scarcely breathing, the tears all gone from her eyes.

"You—knew!" she said slowly, at last.

"Yes, I knew," he said. He looked deep into her eyes for seconds, and then she felt him drawing her irresistibly to him. She yielded herself as driftwood yields to a racing flood, no longer caring for the interpretation of the riddle, scarcely remembering its existence; heard him laugh above her head—a brief, exultant laugh—as he clasped her. And then came his lips upon her own. . . .

"You see, dear," he said later, a quiver that was not all laughter in his voice, "it is not so remarkably wonderful, after all, that I should know all about it, when you come to consider that I was there—there with you in the magic circle all the time."

"You were there!" she echoed, turning in his arms. "But how was it I never knew? Why did I not see you?"

"Faith, sweetheart, I think you did!" said Sir Roland. Then, at her quick cry of amazed understanding: "I wanted to teach you a lesson, but, sure, I'm thinking it's myself that learned one, after all." And, as she clung to him, still hardly believing: "We have found our paradise together, my Lady Una," he whispered softly. "And, love, there is no way back."

YPRES

(September, 1915)

By Arthur Conan Doyle

Drawings by

L. Raven-Hill

Push on, my Lord of Wurtemburg, push on, across the fen!
  See where the lure of Ypres calls you!
There's just one ragged British line of Plumer's weary men,
It's true they held you off before, but venture it again!
  Come, try your luck, whatever fate befalls you!

You've been some little time, my Lord. Perhaps you scarce remember
  The far-off early days of that resistance.
Was it in October last? Or was it in November?
And now the leaves are turning and you stand in mid-September
  Still staring at the Belfry in the distance.

Can you recall the fateful day—a day of drifting skies,
  When you started on the famous Calais onset?
Can it be the War-Lord blundered when he urged the enterprise?
For surely it's a weary while since first before your eyes
  That old Belfry rose against the sunset.

You held council at your quarters, when the budding Alexanders,
  And the Pickel-haubed Cæsars gave their reasons.
Was there one amongst that bristle-headed circle of commanders,
Ever ventured the opinion that a little town of Flanders
  Would hold you pounded here through all the seasons!

You all clasped hands upon it.   You would break the British line,
　　You would smash a road to westward with your host,
The howitzers should thunder and the Uhlan lances shine,
Till Calais heard the blaring of the distant "Wacht am Rhein,"
　　As you topped the grassy uplands of the coast.

And so next day your battle rolled across the Menin Plain,
　　Where Capper's men stood lonely to your wrath.
You broke him, and you broke him, but you broke him all in vain,
For he and his contemptibles kept closing up again,
　　And the khaki bar was still across your path.

And on the day when Gheluvelt lay smoking in the sun,
　　When Von Deimling stormed so hotly in the van,
You smiled as Haig reeled backwards and you thought him on the
　　run,
But, alas for dreams that vanish, for before the day was done,
　　It was you, my Lord of Wurtemburg, that ran.

A dreary day was that—but another came, more dreary,
　　When the Guard from Arras led your fierce attacks,
Spruce and splendid in the morning were the Potsdam Grenadiere,
But not so spruce that evening when they staggered spent and weary,
　　With those cursed British storming at their backs.

You knew—your spies had told you—that the ranks were scant and
　　thin,
　　That the guns were short of shell and very few,
By all Bernhardi's maxims you were surely bound to win,
There's the open town before you.   Haste, my Lord, and enter in,
　　Or the War-Lord may have telegrams for you.

Then came the rainy winter, when the price was ever dearer,
　　Every time you neared the prize of which you dreamed,
Each day the Belfry faced you, but you never brought it nearer,
Each night you saw it clearly, but you never saw it clearer.
　　Ah what a weary time it must have seemed!

At last there came the Easter when you loosed the coward gasses,
　　Surely you have got the rascals now!
You could see them spent and choking as you watched them thro'
　　your glasses,
Yes, they choke, but never waver, and again the moment passes,
　　Without one leaf of laurel for your brow.

Fair Ypres was a relic of the soul of other days,
A poet's dream, a wanderer's delight.

Then at Hooge you had them helpless, for their guns were one to ten,
  And you blasted trench and traverse at your will.
You had them dead and buried, but they still sprang up again;
"Donnerwetter!" cried your Lordship, "Donnerwetter!" cried your
    men,
  For their very ghosts were guarding Ypres still.

Active, Guards, Reserve—men of every corps and name
  That the bugles of the War-Lord muster in.
Each in turn you tried them, but the story was the same;
Play it how you would, my Lord, you never won the game,
  No, never in a twelvemonth did you win.

A year, my Lord of Wurtemburg—a year, or nearly so,
  Since first you faced that British *vis-à-vis*.
Your learned Commandanten are the men who ought to know,
But to ordinary mortals it would seem a trifle slow,
  If you really mean to travel to the sea.

If you cannot *straf* the British, since they *strafen* you so well,
  You can safely smash the town that lies so near,
So it's down with arch and buttress, down with belfry and with bell,
And it's *hoch* the seven-seven that can drop the petrol shell
  On the shrines that pious hands have loved to rear!

Fair Ypres was a relic of the soul of other days,
  A poet's dream, a wanderer's delight.
We will keep it as a symbol of your brute Teutonic ways,
That millions yet unborn may come and curse you as they gaze
  At this token of your impotence and spite.

For shame, my Lord of Wurtemburg! Take heart! across the fen,
  See where the little army calls you.
It's just the old familiar line of fifty thousand men;
They've beat you once or twice, my Lord, but venture it again,
  Come, try your luck, whatever fate befalls you.

JOURNEY'S END

By Jeffery Farnol

Drawings by
S. Abbey

I

"You are a stranger in these parts, I think, sir?" said the landlord, glancing round his trim inn parlour with its neatly sanded floor, its raftered ceiling, its big, wide chimney, and the rows of glittering pewter that adorned its walls, and back to the wayworn and dusty traveller hungrily occupied with his food.

He was a very tall man, was this traveller, deep of chest and broad of shoulder, and with a face burned and tanned. His expression, naturally stern, was rendered more so by a scar upon one cheek, and altogether there was an air about him of tireless action, and conflict with man and circumstance. Yet there was also a kindly light in his dark, long-lashed eyes, and his mouth was broad and humorous; wherefore, as he set down his tankard, the landlord made bold to repeat his question:

"You're a stranger hereabouts, sir?"

"Yes and no," answered the traveller.

"Meaning, sir?"

"That I lived in this part of the country—many years ago."

"You've been a traveller, eh, sir, in furrin' parts?"

"Yes, I have seen a good deal of the world."

"A sailor p'r'aps, sir, or a soldier?" said the landlord, with his glance upon the traveller's scarred cheek.

"I have been both in my time—and many things besides."

"Lord!" exclaimed the landlord, hitching his chair a little nearer, "think o' that now! Soldiers I've knowed, and sailors I've knowed, but I never knowed nobody as had been a sailor and a soldier."

"I've lived a harder life than most men," said the traveller.

"And as to—hactive service now?" pursued the landlord, more and more interested,—"wars, sir—battle, murder, and sudden death, —you've seen plenty of haction—eh, sir?"

"I have had my share of it," said the traveller, turning to help himself to more beef from the big joint before him.

"And as to—travels now—you know Hindia, p'r'aps?"

"Yes, I've been to India."

"Ah!—and Hafrica?"

"And Africa," nodded the traveller.

"And China,—what about China?"

" Yes, I have been in China."

" Why, then—p'r'aps you might happen to know—America ? "

" Yes."

" What—you do ? "

" Yes."

" Why, then, I had a brother once as went to America—Peter Adams he were called—though his baptismal name were John. P'r'aps you might 'ave seen him there, sir, or heard tell of him ? "

" America is very large ! " said the traveller, smiling, and shaking his head.

" Aye, but so were my brother," nodded the landlord : " a fine, strapping chap—almost as tall as you be, sir, and by trade a blacksmith, and very like me except for him having whiskers and me none, and his hair being dark and mine light ; still the family resemblance were very strong."

The traveller smiled, and shook his head as he pushed away his plate, and his smile was good to see.

" No," he answered, " I never ran across your brother in America that I know of. But now, seeing I have answered all your questions, let me ask you a few."

" Surely, sir—sure-ly ! "

" First then, do you know Sparkbrook Farm ? "

" Ah, to be sure I do—gets all my eggs and butter there."

" Who owns it ? "

" Farmer Stebbins, sir."

This answer seemed unwelcome to the traveller, for his thick, black brows contracted, and he sighed.

" How long has Farmer Stebbins lived there ? "

" Oh, this seven year and more."

" And what has become of—of the former owner ? "

" Meaning old Prendergast — him we called 'the Squire,' sir ? "

" Yes."

" Died, sir ;—his widder sold the place to Stebbins, and then she died too."

" Ah ! And what became of the—the others ? "

" Meaning the darters, sir ? Well, they went to live over Tenterden way — and got married."

" Both of them ? "

" Why, 'ow might you come to know that there was two darters ? "

" Both of them ? "

" Well, I won't swear to so much as that, but Annabel did—least-ways, if it wasn't Annabel, it were Marjorie as did—married a young farmer over Horsmonden way——"

" Then you're not sure—which one got married ? " said the traveller, fixing the landlord with his piercing eyes.

" Not sure ; no, sir."

" And they're living, you say, at Horsmonden ? "

" Ah !—leastways they was last time I heard on 'em."

" And how far is it to Horsmonden ? "

" 'Bout eight mile, sir."

" Thank you ! " said the traveller, and rose.

" What, be you a-going there, sir ? "

" I am. How much do I owe you for my very excellent meal ? "

And, after the traveller had settled his bill, he took up his hat and stick, and crossed over to the door.   But upon the threshold he paused.

" You say you can't remember which it was ? "

" Meaning—as got married ?—no, sir, I can't. Ye see they was both fine, handsome young maids, and they both had many offers, so it's like as not as they both got——"

" Good-bye ! " said the traveller, rather hastily, and turned on his heel.

" Stay a bit, sir," said the landlord, following him into the road. " If your 'eart be set on Horsmonden then your best way is across the fields ; it be two mile shorter, that way."

" How do I go ? "

" You foller this highroad till you be come to the first stile on your right ; you climb over that, and foller the path till you be come to a bridge over a brook ; you cross that bridge and go on till you be come to another stile ; you climb over that——"

" Thank you ! " nodded the traveller, and turned away.

" —And foller the path again till you be come to a wood," continued the landlord. " You leave the wood on your left——"

" I see," said the traveller, beginning to quicken his steps.

" —No, I mean your right," the landlord went on, his voice rising with the traveller's every stride ; " you climbs over two more stiles, you crosses another brook, and Horsmonden lays straight afore you."

Hereupon the traveller nodded again, flourished his stick, and walked rapidly away.

" Well ! " said the landlord, watching his long, easy stride, " well, if ever there was a impatient man in this here vale o' sorrer, there goes the impatientest ! "

II

Meanwhile the traveller continued his way at the same rapid pace, crossing the stile as he had been directed; but, for the most part, he walked with bent head and a frown of thought upon his dark brow. Earlier in the day he had gazed with greedy eyes upon the well-remembered beauties of green valley and wooded hill, and had gloried in it all,—the warmth of the sun, the soft wind sweet with the fragrance of honeysuckle and new-mown hay, and the thousand delicious scents of hidden flowers and dewy soil; pausing to listen to the bubbling music of some brook, to stare into the cool, green depths of woods thrilled with the song of thrush or blackbird; and had known that boundless content that only the returned exile can appreciate or understand.

But now? Now he strode on, blind and deaf to it all, faster and faster, eager only to reach the end of that journey which had led him across half the world. And as he walked, he thought of the struggle and tumult of these latter years,—the sufferings and hardships endured, the dangers outfaced, the bitter trials and disappointments, and the final realisation. But now—what were fortune and success but empty sounds, what but a mockery all his riches, if disappointment waited for him—at the journey's end?

So lost was he amid these whirling thoughts that he presently found that, despite the landlord's precise directions, he had missed his way, for he became aware that he was traversing a very narrow, grassy lane that wound away on each hand apparently to nowhere in particular. He stopped, therefore, and was looking about him in some annoyance when he heard the voice of a crying child, and going a little way along the lane, saw a little girl who sat demurely in the shade of the hedge, stanching her tears with the aid of a torn and bedraggled pinafore.

Now, as he looked down at her, and she looked up at him over the tattered pinafore, with two large tears balanced and ready to fall, the traveller found himself very much at a loss—since, hitherto in his varied experiences, small feminine persons who lamented with the aid of tattered pinafores had had no part. However, being a polite traveller, he raised his hat, and smiled. Whereupon the small person, forgetful of her sorrow, smiled up at him; for, despite the big stick he carried, and his strange, dark face with its fierce black brows and the ugly mark upon the bronzed cheek, there was something in the long-lashed eyes, and the gentle curve to the firm, clean-shaven lips, that seemed to take her fancy, for she nodded her curly head at him approvingly.

"I'm awful glad you've come!" she sighed; "I've been waiting and waiting, you know."

" Oh, really ? " said he, more at a loss than ever.

" Yes, I need somebody dre'fful bad, that's nice an' tall an' big, like you," she nodded, " an' I was 'fraid you'd never come, you know."

" Ah, yes—I see ; and is that why you were crying ? "

" I wasn't—crying," she answered, with scornful emphasis on the verb. " Ladies never cry—they weep, you know—an' I just sat down here to shed a few tears."

" Ah, to be sure ! And why were you weeping ? "

" Well, I was weeping because my poor Norah got herself caught in the hedge, an' when I tried to get her down I tore my very best pinafore, an'—scratched my—poor—dear—little finger ! " And here-upon at the recollection of these woes the two tears (having apparently made up their minds about it) immediately cast themselves overboard, and lost themselves in the folds of the tattered pinafore.

" Can I help you ? "

" If you'll please reach Norah down out of that thorny hedge,— there she is ! "

Looking in the direction indicated, he saw a pink-cheeked doll, very small of mouth, and very large and round of eye, who, despite her most unfortunate situation among the brambles, seemed to be observing a butterfly that hovered near by, with a stoic philosophy worthy of Zeno himself.

In the twinkling of an eye Norah was rescued from her precarious perch, and held out to her small, rapturous mother ; but, before she reached those little anxious hands, the traveller's hold suddenly relaxed, and poor Norah fell into the ditch.

" Child," said he, his voice sudden and sharp, " what is your name ? "

But she was too busy rescuing and comforting the unfortunate Norah to answer a great, big, clumsy man's foolish questions just then.

" Who are you ? " repeated the traveller, staring into the pretty flushed face that was no longer hidden in the pinafore.

" Did a nasty, big, dusty man frow her into the ditch then ! "

" Child," said the traveller more gently, and stooping to look into the violet eyes, " tell me your name."

" My name," she answered, with much hauteur, and pausing to smooth Norah's ruffled finery, " is Marjorie."

" Marjorie ! " he repeated, and then again, " Marjorie ! " and stood leaning on his stick, his broad shoulders stooping and his eyes staring away blindly into the distance.

" Yes, Marjorie," she repeated, " just like my Ownest Own."

" Do you mean your—mother ? " he asked, with a strange hesi-tation at the word.

" Yes, my mother ; but I call her my Ownest Own 'cause she belongs all to me, you see. My Ownest Own lives with me—over there," she

went on, pointing up the lane, "all alone with old Anna, 'cause Father has to work in the big city, oh, a long, long way off—in a train, you know. But he comes to see me sometimes, an' always brings me s'prises—in parcels, you know. Norah was a s'prise he brought me 'cause I was seven last week. An' now," said she, changing the subject abruptly, "now I'm all tired an' worn out—so please take me home."

"No, I don't think I can take you home. You see I must be going."

"Going! but where?"

"Oh, a long, long way—in a train and a ship," said the traveller, with his gaze still on the distance.

"But please, I want you to come an' help Norah over the stiles; she finds them so very trying, you know—an' so do I."

But the traveller sighed, and shook his head.

"Good-bye, Marjorie!" he said gently.

"Are you going to leave me—all alone, an' you've only just found me?"

"I must!"

"Well, then," said Marjorie, nodding her small head at him resolutely, "I shall sit down under the hedge again, an' weep—very loud!" —which she straightway proceeded to do, so that her lamentations frightened an inquisitive blackbird that had hopped audaciously near to stare at them with his bold, bright eye.

"Hush!" said the traveller, much perturbed, falling on his knees beside her, "hush, Marjorie—don't do that!" But still she wept, and still she wailed, with Norah clasped tight in her arms, until at length he yielded in sheer desperation.

"Very well," he said, stroking her glossy curls with a touch that was wonderfully light and gentle for a hand so very big, "I'll go with you."

"I thought you would," she nodded, promptly smiling at him through her tears; "then please hold Norah a minute while I put on my sun-bonnet." And when she had tied her bonnet-strings exactly under the dimple in her chin, she held up her arms for Norah, and they set off along the lane together.

She slipped her warm fingers into his and remarked casually, "I like you 'cause you are so big an' tall, you know. My Ownest Own says that all great, big men are good an' kind, 'cause they are so big, —an' my Ownest Own knows all about everything—an' that's why I'm taking you home to her."

But here he stopped, and glanced down at his guide in sudden trepidation:

"Taking me—home—to—her!" he repeated, slowly.

"Oh yes, I'm taking you as a s'prise. You see," she went on, "to-day is my Ownest Own's birthday, so I came out to try an' find a s'prise for her, an' I looked an' looked, but I couldn't find anything, an' then Norah got caught in the hedge, an' I wept. An' then you heard me, an' then, when I saw you, I thought you'd do for a s'prise 'cause you're so big an' tall, so I'm taking you to my Ownest Own for a birfday s'prise present."

"But," said he, still hesitating, "supposing she shouldn't happen to—like me?"

"Oh, but she will!" returned Marjorie, nodding the big sunbonnet complacently. "My Ownest Own always loves my s'prises, you see, an' you are such a big one—though you are a bit dusty, you know."

"Tell me more about her. Is she happy—your—mother?"

"Oh yes; she's got me, you see, an' old Anna, an' the Marquis—he's the parrot—an' we're all as happy as happy. 'Course she weeps sometimes, but all ladies weep now an' then, you know—I do myself."

At last they came in sight of a cottage. It was small, but neat and trim, and stood in a wide garden of flowers and fruit-trees, inclosed by a tall hedge of clipped yew, in which there was a small gate. Beside this wicket was a large tree, in the shadow of which the traveller stopped.

"Richard!" cried a sharp, querulous voice—"Richard! Richard!"

"Who is that?" he exclaimed, glancing about.

"Oh, it's only the Marquis," Marjorie answered, laughing to see how this great big man started at the sound; "it's the parrot, you know. Now you please stay here," she went on, "while I go an' find my Ownest Own, an' don't come till I call you, an'—— Why, there she is!"

But the traveller had already seen a tall, graceful figure coming slowly toward them through the flowers. Leaning one hand against the tree for support, he looked with hungry eyes upon the proud beauty of her whose memory had been with him in the hum and bustle of strange cities, in the loneliness of prairies, in the fierce tumult of war and conflict—weary years of stress and struggle through which he had fought his way to her until now, upon this golden afternoon, he had reached his journey's end. The child Marjorie—her child!—stood between them, smiling up at him with finger raised admonishingly as she bade him keep quiet. And, in this moment, the bitterness of all the past seemed concentrated, and he leaned more heavily against the tree. But, though he uttered no sound, suddenly, as if she divined his presence, Marjorie, the woman, looked up, and saw him—and uttered a broken cry and ran toward him with hands outstretched, and stopped, breathing quick, and so they gazed upon each other for a long, silent minute.

"Richard!" she said at last, in the voice of one who dreams—"Richard!"

6

" I have—come back—you see," said he, his voice harsh and uneven.

" I thought you were—dead, Richard."

" Yes, it was a long time for you to wait—too long, I know now—but I have come back to you, Marjorie, as I told you I would."

" But you never wrote—all these long, long years ! "

" I did—yes, I did at first. I sent you three letters."

" I never got them."

" That was part of my ill fortune."

" Why did you ever go ? We all believed in you, Richard. Even father, in his heart of hearts, knew you could never have stooped to take the money ; and the real thief was caught soon after, and confessed ;—why did you go, Richard ? "

" I was a proud young fool ! " said he, bitterly.

" We advertised for you in all the papers."

" I have been in places where papers are not known," he answered ; " you see I have lived a lonely life at all times, Marjorie."

" Lonely, Richard ? Do you know what loneliness is, I wonder ?—the endless chain of nights and days and weeks and months and years ; the watching and hoping and praying, and the soul-destroying disappointment ? "

" And we were to have been married—in a fortnight ! " said he dully : " how impossible it all seems—now ! And yet, all these years I have hoped and dreamed that it might yet be—that the more I endured of hardship and disappointment, the more surely should I find happiness waiting for me—at the journey's end."

" Then you—did—still care, Richard ? "

" Care ! " His voice thrilled through her, and she saw how the strong brown hand quivered upon the tree.

" You had not—forgotten ? "

" Your memory has been with me always, Marjorie," he answered, speaking in the same low, repressed tone, " and always will be—even though I am too late."

" Too late ? "

" I waited too long," he went on, not looking at her now ; " I hoped, and expected too much of Fortune ; my journey does not end here, as I prayed it might. I must go on and on, until my time is accomplished—but your memory will go with me to the end, Marjorie."

" Richard—what do you mean ? "

" I mean that the hand which led me here was the hand of your child—whose father works in the city."

" My child—Marjorie ? " Now, as she spoke, her eyes, that had hitherto sought his face as the face of one come back from the dead, wavered and fell, the colour deepened in her cheek again and her bosom rose with a long, fluttering sigh. She turned slowly and went toward him ; but, in that same moment, the quiet was suddenly dispelled by the wailing lamentation of the child, seated sedately beneath the hedge, with Norah clasped tight in her arms. In an instant Marjorie was down upon her knees beside her, all soft caresses and tender solicitude, whereat the wailing gradually subsided.

"I'm all right now, my Ownest Own," she said, smoothing Norah's rumpled frock; "I only thought you'd forgot all 'bout me. You see, I went an' found you such a nice, big s'prise—though he is a bit dusty, I know—an' you never even said, 'Thank you very much.'"

"Thank you, darling, thank you!" and the two Marjories kissed each other.

"He wouldn't let me bring him at first 'cause he was 'fraid you wouldn't like him, you know; but you do, don't you, my Ownest Own?"

"Yes, dear."

"You like him lots, an' lots—don't you?"

"Yes, dear."

"An' you thank me for him very much—don't you?"

"And I thank you very much."

"Very well!" sighed the small autocrat, "now we're all happy again, an' please take me in to tea, 'cause I'm dre'fful hungry, my Ownest Own."

III

Richard Carmichael, in his wanderings to and fro in the waste places of the world, had fronted death many times in one shape or another, he had met disaster calm-eyed, and trampled terror underfoot; yet never had he more need of his stern self-repression and iron will than now, as he sipped his tea in the pleasant shade of the fruit-trees, listening to the merry chatter of the child, and answering the many questions of the woman, glancing at her but seldom, yet aware of her every look and gesture, even while he turned to minister to the numerous wants of the child, or to kiss the pink-cheeked doll, at her imperious command.

"You are very quiet, Richard!"

"Why, I was never much of a talker—even in the old days, Marjorie," he answered, and there was a touch of bitterness in his tone because of the radiant light in her eyes and the thrill of happiness in her voice. The hope that he had cherished in his heart all these years was dead; his dream was ended; he was awake at last, and the journey's end was not yet.

"Richard!" screamed the Marquis—"Richard! Richard!"

"Did you teach him to say that, Marjorie?"

"Yes,—the Marquis is quite an accomplished bird, you see. Let me fill up your cup, Richard."

"I've tried to teach him to say my father's name, too, but he won't, you know," said the child.

"Talk, Richard—tell your adventures—what you have done, and where you have been all these years," said Marjorie, rather hastily.

So, perforce, he began to describe the wonders he had seen, the terrors of the wilderness, the solemn grandeur of mighty mountains and rushing rivers, of storm and tempest; he told of strange peoples, and wondrous cities, while she listened wide-eyed and silent.

"And how did you get that scar upon your cheek?" she asked when he paused.

"Trying to arrest a murderer."

"And did you arrest him?"

"Yes."

"Was he hanged?"

"No—it wasn't necessary."

"Do you mean——?"

"Yes."

"Oh, Richard!"

"'Fraid my Norah's getting awful sleepy!" interjected the child at this juncture.

"You are greatly altered, Richard."

"And yet you knew me on the instant."

"You seem—so much colder and—harder."

"I have lived among hard people."

"And so much bigger and stronger."

"That is because I have laboured."

"And—much quieter."

"That is because I am, perhaps, a little wiser."

"Do you think—I am altered, Richard?"

"Yes,—you are more beautiful, I think."

"But you don't look at me, Richard."

"'Fraid my Norah's nearly asleep now!" sighed the child again, stifling a yawn very politely, "an' 'fraid I am too."

"So you are, sweetheart," said Marjorie; "say 'Good-night,' and your Ownest Own will take you up to bed."

"Good-night—Richard!" said the small person demurely, and held up her mouth to be kissed.

"Good-bye!" returned the traveller, bending his dark head down to hers, "Good-bye, little Marjorie!" And, when he had kissed her, he rose and stretched out his hand toward his hat and stick.

"But—you're not going to go, Richard?" said the child, planting herself before him.

"Yes."

"Do you mean—in a train, an'—a ship?"

"Yes, Marjorie."

"Oh! but you mustn't, you know," she said, shaking her curls at him; "you must make him stay, my Ownest Own, 'cause I shall be sure to want him—to-morrow."

"Do you mean that you are really—going—back, Richard?" asked, Marjorie.

"Yes, to the wilderness; it's the only place for me, Marjorie."

"Then, Richard—at least—wait—a little while."

"Wait?"

"Until I have tucked little Sleepy-head up in bed," she answered, rising. "I shan't be long; stay where you are, and—wait."

"Wait?" said he again.

"I have—something I want to tell you," she said, not looking at him now; and, as she turned away, he noticed, for the first time, that she still wore her gardening gloves. So he sat down again, and watched the two Marjories go up the long, flower-bordered walk together until they entered the cottage.

To wait? To look into her eyes again? To have her once more within reach of his arms? To listen a few moments longer to the sweet, low tones of her voice, and then—to go? No—a thousand times! Better to slip away, now, in the silence, unseen; yes, better so—much better than the cold, dead memory of a formal leave-taking.

Wherefore, upon the instant, up sprang the blundering traveller, and snatching hat and stick, hurried down the path and through the gate. But once in the lane and out of sight of the cottage, his stride slackened and his feet dragged wearily, and as he came to a small coppice he turned in among the trees and threw himself face downward in the grass.

But in a few minutes he was startled by a woman's voice, calling his name.

He started to his feet to find her standing there amid the green, flushed of cheek and panting with her haste.

"Why did you go away, Richard?"

"Because I was—afraid."

"Afraid?"

"Of myself! Oh, why have you followed me?" he cried passionately; "don't you understand me?—can't you see? I love you, Marjorie; I loved you as a boy—to-day I am a man, and, with the years, with all I have endured, my love has grown until it fills the world. Go back!—you must go back—to your child—and his, and leave me to go on—to the journey's end."

"Richard!" she said gently, "if you have been faithful all these years don't you think—I have?"

"What do you mean?" he demanded, huskily. For answer she reached out her hands to him, and then he saw that she no longer wore her gloves,—he saw also that her white fingers were without a ring.

"Marjorie! What do you mean?" he repeated.

"I mean that I am even as you left me; I mean that no man's lips have ever pressed mine; I mean that I am as much yours to-day as ever I was."

"But—the child?"

"The child!" she laughed, brokenly; "she was my sister Annabel's, who died at her birth, and I have tried to take her place. Yes, I know I let you think otherwise — because I — I wanted to be sure you —cared, Richard; I wanted to see you—suffer—just a little, Richard, because I have suffered so very long. And then, when I came back to tell you —you had gone. And then a great fear came to me, and I followed you—I ran all the way, Richard—and—and—that's all; only you will forgive me for wanting to see you suffer—just a little?"

"Forgive you!— Oh, my Marjorie!" and he caught her hands, and bent his head above them.

"Dick!" she whispered, stooping above him, all warmth and tenderness, — "you great, strong, foolish Dick, to think that I could ever have forgotten you! You will never leave me again?"

"No," he answered, clasping her to him; "I have reached my journey's end."

THE SOOT-FAIRIES
By Beatrice Harraden

Painting and Drawings by
Arthur Rackham, R.W.S.

IT was just about tea-time, and the light was growing dim in the old schoolroom; but the glow from the fire fell upon the face of a little girl, who was sitting on the hearth, in company with her doll, and a white kitten, and a fairy-book. She threw down the book, and said rather impatiently:

"I don't believe one bit in these stupid fairies, and I'm tired of fairy-books; yes, and I'm tired of dolls, too, and of white kittens, too; and I hate every one and everything!"

Having delivered herself of this amiable speech, she pushed away the white kitten, which had been playing with her soft brown hair, and she took up her doll, at which she gazed critically for several seconds.

"You are an ugly thing, Arabella Stuart," she remarked, "and I am surprised that I have ever been fond of you. Oh dear me! I wish it were tea-time."

Suddenly, to her surprise and disgust, a quantity of soot fell down the chimney.

"How horrible that soot is!" she said to the white kitten, and moved her seat farther away from the fireplace. Then she added: "You had better come too, dear, as the smuts will make you quite black, and I shouldn't like to see your beautiful coat black instead of white. I don't want to see you look like a sweep. Dear me, how teasing those smuts are!"

Just at that moment she heard angry voices, calling her name impatiently:

"Really, Beryl, you're very rude! What is the use of our taking the trouble to come down the chimney to see you, if you move away and say insulting things about us? A nice kind of a hostess you are, to be sure!"

Beryl looked round and saw, to her astonishment, that what she had mistaken for a mass of soot was really a dense crowd of little black persons who began distributing themselves in all directions, flying on to the white kitten and making him look like a Hottentot, flying on to the beautiful clothes she was making for Arabella Stuart, and literally covering her own white apron. She tried to appear as pleasant as she could under the circumstances, and said:

"Please tell me who you are?"

71

" Why, we're the soot-fairies," they answered. " Who else should we be ? "

" Oh, if you're fairies," Beryl answered eagerly, " I'm very pleased indeed to see you all ; but I thought you were what we call ' blacks ' or ' smuts,' and I was just going to brush you all away."

" Beryl," said one little soot-lady, who had been flying about in the air and now perched herself on Beryl's nose, " let me tell you one very important thing. You should never brush away a smut, because, for all you know, you might be hurting a fairy. I don't say that *all* smuts are fairies, dear ; but still, it *is* best to be on the safe side. At any rate, if you must brush away the smut, do it as gently as possible."

" I will certainly remember," said Beryl, suppressing an inclination to brush the soot-fairy off her nose. She was glad she had restrained herself, for the little lady flew away of her own accord and came and rested on Beryl's hand. She was the prettiest little thing, dressed in black crape, without a speck of white anywhere. She wore a handsome black pearl necklace.

" Well, dear," she said, " and so you have never heard of the soot-fairies ? How very much you have to learn ! You ought to travel, you know. Nothing like travelling for expanding the mind. Come and pay a visit to our land. It would be a little change for you."

" Where do you live ? " asked Beryl.

The soot-fairy laughed.

" Why, up the chimney, to be sure ! " she answered. " You cannot think how beautiful and black it is up there. I am sure you would enjoy yourself with us, Beryl ! There are no fairies so merry as the soot-fairies. Our black dresses do not interfere with our merry hearts. If you'll come home with me, dear, I'll teach you many things up the chimney, and I'll teach you to fly about just like the soot-fairies fly ; and I really think you'd like the chimney-sweep who comes and visits us occasionally. All chimney-sweeps are not nice, you know, but this one is so gentle and considerate. He knows all about the secrets of the chimney, and he would not hurt one of the soot-fairies. He does not like to disturb us in our homes, and though he is obliged sometimes to take us away in his sack, we like going with him. We cling about his coat, and we dance all over his face, and people say :

" ' Doesn't that chimney-sweep look black ! ' "

" I'm sure I've often said that," said Beryl, smiling.

" Of course you have," laughed the fairy, " because you did not understand. But the chimney-sweep goes on his way laughing, not minding what people say, for he dearly loves the little soot-fairies, and likes them to cling about him. He did not come for a long time, and so one day we asked the new man what had become of our old friend, for we thought he must be ill, since he had forsaken us."

The Soot-Fairies and the Chimney-Sweep who became a Gardener.

73

" And was he ill ? " asked Beryl.

" No," said the fairy ; " the stranger told us he was tired of chimney-sweeping, and that he had become a gardener. That made us very sad, and we determined to go and reproach him. So one day, when the stranger came to fetch us away in a bag, we all escaped, and flew in a crowd to the garden where our friend was working. He looked quite different from his old self ; his face was quite white, and his clothes were not in the least smutty. We swarmed about him, and made such a commotion that he dropped his spade and cried :

" ' Here are the soot-fairies, the dear little soot-fairies ! '

" ' We can't do without you,' we cried as we caressed him. ' There is no chimney-sweep like you. Come back to us, for we're getting quite pale with grief.' "

" And did he come back ? " asked Beryl.

" A few days after," continued the fairy, " we heard the house-maid say that the chimney was to be swept the next morning ; and you can imagine how delighted we were when we heard his voice sing out to us the old greeting :

" ' Dear little soot-fairies, good-morning to you all ! ' "

" Oh, I'm so glad he came back," said Beryl, clapping her hands with delight. " Do you know, I shall never any more be frightened of chimney-sweeps. And I should so like to make his acquaintance."

" And so you shall, dear," said the fairy, " if you come home with me."

Beryl thought, in her heart of hearts, that she would prefer to make the acquaintance of the chimney-sweep this side of the chimney, but she was polite enough to thank the fairy for her kind invitation.

" You'll see wonderful things up the chimney," said the fairy. " We have the most lovely black flowers, with such a delicious scent. Surely you must have smelt the chimney-flowers. There is nothing like them anywhere else."

" I certainly have smelt a sooty smell," thought Beryl, but she kept the thought to herself.

" I must say I should like to go up the chimney," she said after a pause, " if only I could be quite sure of not coming down quite black. Nurse would be so angry with me. But it's true I could have a bath afterwards."

" My dear child," they cried, " it's all quite nonsense to suppose that you would be black because you went up the chimney. It's altogether a mistaken notion to suppose that soot makes things black."

" Perhaps I'm only an ignorant little girl," thought Beryl to herself, " but, unless I'm quite mad, the soot-fairies have made the white kitten black, and they've made my white apron black. But never mind. I must not let them see that I am distressed. And they must be nice, after all, since the chimney-sweep loved them."

So she let them do just as they wished, and she did not interfere with their games with the white kitten. He did not seem to worry much about the alteration in his complexion, but rolled about on the ground, keeping the fairies on the alert to escape being squashed.

Then they got tired of the kitten, and they went and played around the coal-scuttle, which was one of those great brass pans, with a handle to it. At last they said they must be starting for home, and they asked Beryl whether she were willing to accompany them.

"Come along, dear," they urged; "it's such good fun being a soot-fairy. And you don't know how amusing it is to fly about just as you like, and tease people by sitting on their noses, when they don't want you, and when they think they are looking particularly handsome."

"I'll come another day," said Beryl, hesitating.

"No, come now!" said the soot-fairies.

So, as she did not see how she could refuse, she said:

"Very well, I'm ready to go up the chimney; but promise me I shan't become black."

"We promise you!" they cried. "Trust our word: soot-fairies never make any one really, really black."

Beryl felt herself being pushed towards the chimney.

"We've forgotten the white kitten," she cried suddenly. "Do let's go back for it." . . .

Then the soot-fairies seemed to lose hold of her, and to float up the chimney, circling with the smoke; and she heard their voices saying reproachfully:

"Beryl must come to our country another time, when she is willing. She is certainly not willing now. She is making excuses."

"No, I'll come now," she cried, starting up and running towards the fender.

But it was too late, for the soot-fairies had gone beyond recall.

But she could not get those soot-fairies out of her mind, and one evening, two or three weeks later, she decided that she would travel to Soot-land and call on the soot-fairies.

"However *shall* I get up the chimney?" she said to Arabella Stuart, of whom she had not taken any very great notice these last few days.

"Oh, I know," she added. "I'll ask the fire-fairies to help me. They are very intimate with the soot-fairies."

So she leaned over the high fender and whispered: "Dear little fire-fairies, do come and help me to get up the chimney."

"I wonder if they'll take any notice," she thought, as she returned to her stool and put a new bonnet on Arabella Stuart's head.

At that moment a tiny piece of coal flew out of the grate on to the white kitten's back. The white kitten did not seem to mind it in the least, but began to purr loudly, and Beryl saw that a little fire-fairy was seated on the bit of coal. No wonder that the kitten was so pleased.

"Well, my dear," he said to her, "and what can I do for you?"

"You are kind to come," said Beryl, smiling with delight. "I want to pay a call on the soot-fairies this afternoon, and I thought perhaps you would help me to get up the chimney."

"Certainly," said her friend; "and you've just happened to choose the right afternoon, for the soot-fairies sent down this morning to order half an hour's worth of smoke, and, if you like, we will send you up with the smoke. It is very easy and quick travelling."

"Half an hour's worth of smoke!" laughed Beryl; "I never heard of anything so funny. I wish I could order sweets poured into a bag at so much the hour."

"Why, that's how they *do* sell sweets in fairyland," said the fairy. "Well, now, will you come with the smoke?"

"Thank you," said Beryl; "but will you just wait one minute? I should like to take my purse with me, for there is no knowing what expenses one might be put to in a foreign land. I shall take my two-shilling bit, and a new sixpence, and four pennies, and three half-pennies. I think that will be quite enough."

"Now," said the fairy, when Beryl had pocketed her purse, "shut your eyes, my child, and trust entirely to me."

Beryl did as she was told, and found herself landed, together with the cat and the doll, on a large piece of coal in the grate.

"You're only just in time," said some voices. "The smoke is just going to start. It is very pleasant travelling. You simply rise with the smoke, you know, as if you were in an elevator. Don't be at all anxious or nervous. It's the only sensible way of travelling."

"Are you sure I shan't travel right out of the chimney?" said Beryl.

But before she could get an answer to this rather important question, the smoke had started, and she was well on her way into Soot-land. It certainly was very pleasant travelling with the smoke, and Beryl would have liked to go on for miles and miles. Suddenly the smoke stopped, and she found herself in a little dark passage, with not a soul near to help her. She was just wondering what she should do, when a soot-fairy appeared at the end of the passage, holding the daintiest little horn-lantern that Beryl had ever seen.

"If you please," said Beryl, advancing timidly down the passage, "I have come to call on the soot-fairies. I have not a card of my own, and so I have written my name on a piece of paper. Here it is."

"The soot-fairies knew you were coming this afternoon," said the little fairy, "and told me to wait near at hand with this lantern,

The Soot-Fairies' games with the White Kitten.

so as to help you in case you might lose your way in Soot-land. Mortals aren't accustomed to this kind of light."

"I should call it 'this kind of dark,'" said Beryl. "But how thoughtful of the dear soot-fairies."

77

At last they came to the end of the long passage, and the fairy opened the door and announced:

" Beryl."

At the sound of that name, hundreds of soot-fairies rushed forward to greet the little girl, and took her into what appeared to be a great hall, hung with lanterns.

" We are very pleased to see you," cried the soot-fairies, dancing round her. " We never use lanterns for ourselves, but we've lit up our hall in honour of you, and we have plucked our best flowers in honour of you."

" I am sure I don't deserve your kindness," said Beryl, smiling. " I was not at all nice to you the other day, and I can't bear to think that I was rude. Please forgive me."

" Why, we have forgiven you long ago," they said. " No one ever sulks in Soot-land. Ah, what a good thing you have brought the white kitten ! We shall all like to have a game of play with him."

Indeed, they had begun already, and Beryl saw, to her dismay, that the white kitten had become a black kitten. Still, she made no remark, and in the true spirit of a real traveller was quite prepared to accept with perfect good-humour anything that might befall. All the same, she was a little horrified to see that Arabella Stuart had also turned black, and she would have been still more horrified if she could have seen her own face ; but luckily there were no looking-glasses in Soot-land. Then she noticed that the lanterns were gradually being put out, and she asked the reason.

" Oh," said a little lady, " you are getting more accustomed to the dark, and in a few minutes you would not be able to see anything at all if the lanterns were kept burning."

And really it was most curious, for, as the soot-lady had said, the less light there was in the hall, the more clearly could Beryl see. There were pictures on the walls—black pictures, of course, and black vases filled with black flowers, and black tapestry sofas, and comfortable black satin cushions.

" Don't the flowers smell delicious ? " said the little soot-lady enthusiastically. " There is no land where the flowers are as beautiful as in Soot-land."

Beryl smelt and smelt, and tried to detect the fragrance of which the soot-fairies spoke ; but all she could smell was soot, nothing but soot !

" Those, dear Beryl, are roses," said the little lady, pointing to a bowl of black flowers.

" Are they ? " said Beryl. " How curious, to be sure. I have never before seen black roses."

" Why, what other colour should they be ? " said the little soot-lady. " And these are geraniums."

"Black geraniums!" laughed Beryl. "I never heard of such a thing."

"Why, you wouldn't expect them to be red?" said the soot-fairy rather sharply. "And these, as you see, are daffodils."

"Black daffodils!" cried Beryl, who was nearly getting out of temper. "Why, daffodils are yellow, and lilies-of-the-valley are white."

"My dear child," said the soot-fairy, "you are making a sad mistake; you evidently know nothing at all about flowers, and so I shall not take the trouble to argue with you. You ought to learn a little botany."

"I hope I have not been rude," said Beryl anxiously; "but everything is so different in my country."

"Of course it is," said the little lady. "I had forgotten that. Come along now. There is the dinner bell ringing, and we are never unpunctual in Soot-land."

Beryl was rather terrified when she heard that she was expected to eat a soot-dinner, but she did her best to behave properly, and, as events proved, she had no cause to complain of the dinner, for indeed it was the most delicious meal she had ever eaten.

First of all there was black soup, and then there was black salmon, and black lobster-sauce; and then there was black turkey, and, of course, black bread-sauce; and there were black jellies, and black ice creams, and, for dessert, most delicious black strawberries and black peaches.

"After all," thought Beryl to herself, as she was enjoying all these luxuries, "colour is nothing."

At this moment the last lantern was extinguished, and one of the soot-fairies rose to propose Beryl's health.

"Health and happiness to dear little Beryl!" cried the soot-fairies as they clinked their black glasses together.

Of course Beryl had to reply, and she felt a little nervous when she rose up and faced the assembled company.

"I am sure I am very much obliged to you," she said, "and I wish you all happiness and health in return. This is the first dinner party I have ever been at, and I am quite sure that I shall never go to such a nice one again, unless I come to you."

Here the fairies broke out into gratified applause.

"I had no idea," continued Beryl, "that Soot-land was such a nice country; and though I was a little puzzled at first about all the flowers being black, still I can quite understand now that they ought not to be anything else. At first I did not think they smelt at all sweet, but now the fragrance seems to me most delicious. Will you let me come again? Please do."

"That we will!" they answered readily. "We are more than

delighted that you should have enjoyed yourself so much to-night. Travelling is good for every one—isn't it? Come whenever you like, and make yourself quite at home in our country. There are a great many black books in the library which you might like to read; and one day we must take you out into the fields and show you our black sheep."

"You *are* good," said Beryl gratefully. "I myself am thinking of giving a party soon, and I hope you will all come to it."

They told her they would be charmed to visit her, and one of the little ladies ventured to hope she would not send the invitation before a week or two, because by that time her new chiffon dress, the last word in Soot-land fashions, would be finished and ready for wearing.

"And now I think I ought to go," said Beryl regretfully. "I shall be terribly sorry to leave Soot-land. Will you please tell me the time, sir?"

The little fairy thus addressed took out a black watch, and told her that the time was half-past six.

She began to say "goodbye."

"How shall I get home?" she asked. "Is it very far to walk?"

"It *is* possible to walk," said the fairies, "but it is a long way and a steep way; so perhaps we had better send you with the smoke which we will blow down the chimney."

When they got to the end of the narrow passage through which Beryl had come on her arrival in Soot-land, one of the soot-fairies rang up the fire exchange on the telephone, and asked the fire-fairies to send up half a minute's worth of smoke.

"All right," was the answer; and at once the smoke began to rise.

"Are you ready, Beryl?" asked the soot-fairies. "Let yourself go, child, and trust entirely to the fairies."

Then they all began to blow violently, with all the force of their fairy lungs. The smoke came puffing, puffing out into the room, and landed Beryl safely on her own little stool. She came down with rather a thud, and cried:

"Good gracious! I've forgotten the white kitten and Arabella Stuart. I must go up the chimney again." . . .

But when she rubbed her eyes, which the smoke had made rather sore, and when she looked around, she saw the white kitten in all his whiteness sprawling on the hearth, biting Arabella Stuart's left hand.

"Those good little soot-fairies!" she said to herself. "They must have sent the doll and the white kitten down in another puff of smoke."

THE SOOT-FAIRIES.

Beryl and Arabella Stuart.

From a painting by Arthur Rackham, R.W.S.

THE FAILURE
By Joseph Hocking
Drawings by
Fred Pegram

I

MR. JOHN SOUTHWELL, of Southwell, Gilbert, and Tucker, Solicitors of Lincoln's Inn Fields, sat in his office poring over some documents. Evidently he was in a bad temper. A frown had settled upon his brow, his lips were compressed, angry flashes shot from his eyes.

He seemed to be on the point of coming to a momentous decision, but hesitated before taking the final step. More than once a far-away look came into his eyes as though he were remembering something that had taken place years before.

"It's no use," he said aloud, "I can stand it no longer. His mother will——; but there, women are always foolish. This is the last straw."

Still he hesitated, as though he were loth to take the momentous step he contemplated. He sat back in his chair and closed his eyes.

Presently he opened a drawer, from which he took a packet. A few seconds later he was looking at a lock of golden hair and the photograph of a chubby-faced, laughing-eyed boy. The frown passed away from his brow, and his lips became tremulous. For more than a minute he sat gazing, then he turned to the documents which had evidently made him angry.

For some time he seemed in a state of indecision; it might seem as though two forces were fighting within him. Then a knock was heard at the door.

John Southwell hastily put the photograph and lock of hair in the drawer, and placed the documents on the table. He had immediately become the cold, calculating man of business again.

"Come in," he said, whereupon the door opened and a young fellow of perhaps twenty-two years of age stood before him.

Again angry flashes shot from John Southwell's eyes. The appearance of the young man at that moment was fateful. Probably if he had waited five minutes longer the history of his life had been different.

"It's you, is it?" said John Southwell sternly. "I was——"

"Look here, pater," interrupted the other. "I want to explain. I had no idea when——"

It was the father's turn to interrupt now, and he held up his hand as he did so.

" I do not want explanations, Jack," he said. " I have listened to them for years, and they have never been satisfactory. What I want is not explanations, but obedience; not excuses, but good behaviour, and hard, steady, plodding work. Unless you have come to assure me that—— but what's the use? What are your promises worth ? "

The young fellow's eyes flashed. Evidently he too had a temper.

" You've no right to say that," he said.

Perhaps it was the tone in his son's voice, or it might be the defiant attitude he adopted which caused every suggestion of tenderness to pass from the older man's face; in any case, John Southwell rose from his chair, went to the door and carefully closed it, and then turned towards his son.

" I've a few things to say to you," he said harshly, " and then we are coming to a definite understanding. I've reached the end of my patience, and can stand no more of this disgrace."

" Disgrace ! "

" Yes, disgrace; be silent and listen."

A hard, angry look came into Jack Southwell's eyes. He was evidently in no mood for admonition.

" From the time you were twelve years old," said John Southwell, " you have been a continuous trouble to me. At your preparatory school you were in constant disgrace. You were refractory, disobedient, and lazy; but for the fact that the head master could not afford to offend me, he would have refused to keep you."

" But—but——" cried Jack.

" You know what my plans were," went on his father. " You have known all your life that I intended you to be a lawyer. I told you repeatedly that you could study for the bar, in which case I should be able to give you such opportunities as but one young barrister in a thousand gets; or you could take your place in this firm—one of the best in London."

" I know, pater, but——"

" I want no buts; you know it was so. Although I had a difficulty in doing so, I got you into Rugchester College, one of the best public schools in England. What was your story there ? I have been looking over some of your reports. I wonder at my patience as I read them. You were almost always at the bottom of your form. Term after term it was always the same. Here you are: 'Greek: shows neither application nor interest. Latin: Careless and inattentive. Literature——' But there, what's the use of reading any more ? Year after year it was the same."

" I begged you to let me go on the military side; if you had——"

"I didn't send you to Rugchester to prepare you for the army, and you know it. At seventeen, instead of being in the Upper Fifth, or the Sixth, as I had hoped and planned, you were still in the Fourth."

"But I got both my cricket and Rugger School Caps," cried Jack triumphantly.

"But for that I don't believe Dr. Merrill would have allowed you to stay at the school," said John Southwell bitterly. "Your School Caps indeed! as though I paid something like £200 a year for you to get those things! My friend Tunstall's boy, who was more than a year younger than you, got triumphantly into the Sixth while you barely scraped into the Fifth."

"Yes, and what a miserable little rat Tunstall always was!" cried Jack.

"He got first-class classical honours at Oxford," cried the father, "and now has a fine Government appointment, while you——"

He checked himself for a moment and then went on.

"I had to pay for a lot of special coaching in order to enable you to pass your 'little-go' at Cambridge. Still, I determined to give you every chance. You are my only son, and—— But what's the use of my going on? You were practically sent down from Cambridge, disgraced. A useless ninny, a hooligan; you got into all sorts of scrapes, and I had to pay for your—your tom-foolery."

The father strode across the office as though his anger kept him from sitting still.

"I want to do you justice," he said. "I never found you out in a lie; you never tried to deceive me. You had sufficient good feeling to own up to what you did. Perhaps that was because you had no shame; still, there it is, and I give you all the credit you can claim for it."

"You accuse me of disgracing you," cried Jack. "When did I ever disgrace you? when did I ever act dishonourably to any man— or woman?"

"Don't you disgrace me by being a failure? Don't you dishonour me by being sent down from Cambridge? Weren't you always playing disgraceful tricks there? Didn't you—but I won't go into that; it's too painful."

"I did nothing disgraceful," cried the young fellow hotly. "I know I was idle: I was never cut out for a student. I know I went in for larks too, and—and got into a lot of messes because of them; but I meant nothing wrong, and——"

"There there," cried the father impatiently, "what's the use of talking about it? You came down from Cambridge a wastrel, a failure. To use your own words, you were 'pilled' again and again. But for your mother's pleadings and the fact that you hadn't been actually vicious, I would have disowned you at the time. But I was silly, and

I gave you another chance. I took you into my office here. With what results? When have you worked? What trust could I put in you?"

"I was never cut out for a lawyer," cried the young fellow; "I wanted you to give me a chance where I could *do* something. I love the open air. What good could I do by stewing over musty old law-books?"

"Musty old law-books!" cried the father. "It is the finest profession in the world, and—and—— But look at this. I got it this morning. Mr. Schneider, one of my best clients, came to see me yesterday afternoon, and, as I was not in, he asked to see you. You insulted him."

"A German!" cried the youth hotly. "He wanted you to help him in a rotten affair. I told him so. Told him I was sure you would not touch his dirty case."

"You called him a rogue, a swindler," said the father. "Instead of dealing with him diplomatically, you have by your brainlessness lost me a most valuable client. But that is not all. There is something more serious still."

"What is that?" asked Jack.

"You know that I was pleased when you began to pay attention to Mary Edgecumbe. It was what both her father and I hoped for. But George Edgecumbe naturally had to think for his daughter. He has been inquiring about you, and he left this office not half an hour ago."

A new light shone in the young fellow's eyes. He became eager, anxious, nervous.

"What did he say?" he asked.

"He said he would have no wastrel as a husband for his daughter. He is a sensible, responsible man, is Edgecumbe, and he declared that, unless you turned over a new leaf, his doors would be closed against you; that until you showed signs of settling down as a well-behaved, industrious fellow, he forbad you ever to speak to his daughter again."

"He said that? What did he mean?"

"He said that. As to what he meant, I should think it is plain enough. He means what I mean. And this leads me to say my last word. For the future I am going to stand no more nonsense. I meant after I had read Schneider's letter, and heard what George Edgecumbe had to say, to order you out of the office, and to send you about your business. I felt that I had had enough of you, and that, as you made your bed, you must lie on it. But I've determined to give you one more chance."

" And that ? "

" That you settle down at the office here. You will start from the very beginning. You will be here at nine o'clock every morning, and do what you are told to do. You will——"

" Dad, I couldn't do it; I couldn't really. Help me to get an out-of-door job. Set me up on a farm——"

" Either you will do what I have said, or I shall have nothing more to do with you. You must make your choice. Either you will do what I tell you, or you go out of that office never to come in again ; either you will be obedient to my will, or you are no son of mine, and not only this office, but my house, will be closed against you."

For a second the young fellow stood like one transfixed. His square jaw worked nervously, there was a look in his eyes not easy to understand.

" You mean that, dad ? " his voice was suppressed and hoarse.

" I always mean what I say."

Jack Southwell stood still a few seconds without speaking. He seemed to be trying to realise the full signifi-cance of his father's words. He was evidently fighting a battle too.

Presently he had evidently made up his mind.

" Good-bye, dad," he said.

" You mean that you will continue to disobey me ? "

" I mean that I cannot do what you ask. I simply cannot. You might as well ask a paralysed man to run."

" You know the alternative ? "

" Yes; good-bye, dad."

He left the office with bowed head.

II

Concerning what took place in John Southwell's house in Russell Square that night I will not write at length. Mrs. Southwell was a weak, timid woman whose will in the course of years had been com-pletely subjugated to that of her husband. She pleaded for her boy, but pleaded in vain. Neither could she deny what her husband said. Jack Southwell had been a failure. He had been more than a failure. He had set his will against that of his father, he had been an idler, he had paid no heed to his father's commands, and, without being actually vicious, he was regarded by many as dissolute and worthless.

For years John Southwell had threatened his son, but, owing to the pleadings of his wife, he had repeatedly consented, although reluctantly, to give the boy another chance. Now, however, he had refused to be persuaded any more. Years before he had mapped out his son's life. He had decided what he must do and what position he must occupy. Now, after repeated trials, he had shown himself not only a failure but a wastrel, added to which he had actually defied his father to do his worst; the hard, stern man of the law had practically driven his son from home.

"I don't want to hear his name mentioned," said John Southwell to his wife, "I don't want to be reminded of him in any way. I have done my best for him; I have sent him to one of the best schools in the country, I gave him every opportunity of doing well at Cambridge. Again and again have I paid his debts. With what results? You know. After that I took him into my own office, and gave him the chance of becoming a partner in one of the finest firms in London. Of course he would have to work. Naturally, too, he would have to pass his examinations, like any one else; but, that done, he might have had a great future. What thanks did I get? What response did he make? No, I have finished with him. He is no longer a son of mine."

Months passed, and nothing was heard of young Jack Southwell. Whither he had gone, or what he was doing, no one knew. Mrs. Southwell wept bitterly in the privacy of her room, but never dared to tell her sorrows to her husband. John Southwell never mentioned his name. Whatever he thought, he made no man his confidant, although his friends declared that the old lawyer was breaking up fast, and that he had added ten years to his life in a few months.

In the August of 1914 the Great War broke out, and Jack Southwell was forgotten even among the most intimate friends of his family in the great world-struggle. It is said that Mrs. Southwell made constant endeavours to find out her son's whereabouts; but that might only be gossip.

In the September of that year it was rumoured that Jack had been seen drilling in a private's uniform, and Mrs. Southwell, too excited to keep such news to herself, mentioned it to her husband.

"I told you I did not wish to hear his name mentioned again," he said, after he had listened carefully to her recital.

"Yes, yes, I know, John," pleaded the mother, "but I can't help it. Besides, if it is true, it is a noble thing he has done. He has offered his life for what he believed to be right."

"Many of the greatest scapegraces in the country have gone into the army," said the father harshly. "Young fools, knowing nothing of what war means, and thinking that joining the army would give them excitement, have posed as heroes. Besides, think of it! A son of mine a private! A friend of every groom and bootblack in his regiment. But it's just like him."

"It shows that he's alive and well, anyhow," sighed the mother thankfully.

"Perhaps it may be the best thing for him to do," said John Southwell; "if he doesn't desert, he may get killed, and——"

"John, how dare you!" cried the poor woman, losing all control over herself. "You are a brute,—you—you are——" and then she broke into a violent fit of weeping.

"I washed my hands of him months ago," said the lawyer. "Whatever he is, he is of no interest to me; he will never do anything but disgrace himself."

The year 1914 wearily dragged out its days, and the darkest Christmas that England has ever known passed away.

On the eve of the New Year Mrs. Southwell came to her husband with an agonised face. "There," she said, "read that," and she pointed to a name in the list of casualties.

It was under the heading, "Wounded, and Missing; feared dead."

John Southwell spoke no word; but he gave a gasp, as though some one had pierced him with a knife.

Neither the father nor the mother spoke for some time, then the former said:

"It is not likely to be he. If it were, I should have received a private communication from the War Office."

"No," sobbed the mother, "he would not mention your name; he would give no address. Oh, my boy, my boy!"

For some time after that John Southwell was very gentle to his wife. He never spent an evening away from her, he anticipated her every want, and never a harsh word escaped his lips.

He never mentioned his son, however, and it was thought by his friends that he had closed his heart against the boy whom he regarded as a disappointment, and a wastrel. But Mrs. Southwell thought otherwise. One evening, going into the bedroom where Jack had slept years before, she saw him on his knees at the bedside. Before him was the photograph of a chubby-faced boy, and a lock of golden hair. Evidently he was unconscious of his wife's presence, for he continued to gaze at the objects before him. Mrs. Southwell saw too that his body shook convulsively, and she heard him cry hoarsely, "Oh God, if it be possible!—if it be possible!"

She left the room as noiselessly as she had entered it. Her heart, in spite of her sorrow, became lighter, for she had seen into her husband's heart.

Week followed week, and month followed month, and there was no further news of Private John Southwell, who, it was feared, was dead. Mrs. Southwell made many inquiries, but without avail. Beyond the dread lines she had read, the curtain which hung over her son's fate was never lifted.

It was on the evening of the fifth of April that husband and wife sat together by their lonely fireside. Daylight had departed, and the evening was chilly. For a long time they sat together without speaking; on the face of each was a look of gloom. Of whom they were thinking it was not difficult to say. Suddenly a loud double rap was heard at the door.

John Southwell took a bunch of keys from his pocket and went into the hall. He never allowed servants to open the letter box. A few seconds later he returned with a look of wild excitement in his eyes.

"Martha! Wife!" he said. "No, it can't be true! May God grant it is!"

"What is it, John? Tell me quickly!"

He held an official-looking document in his hands, and was reading eagerly.

"It's, it's—oh God—it is!"

"Tell me what it is, John. Don't keep me in suspense!"

"It's about—— Oh, bother my spectacles! They are so blurred that I can't read. I only had them attended to last week either—newly sighted by the oculist."

He rubbed his spectacles with trembling hands, the tears rolling down his face, while Mrs. Southwell, unable to restrain herself, snatched the document from him.

"John, he's not dead!" she cried. "Look! listen! It's from his Colonel! He says our Jack's a hero; that his bravery is the watchword of his battalion. And, oh John, he's not a private! He was made a lieutenant in the New Year. And oh—he's—he's—to have the Victoria Cross! Oh, my husband! my boy! His Colonel says he's accomplished almost impossible deeds of heroism; that he's heartened his men under the most terrible conditions; that—that—Oh! I can't read any more. I'm too happy! Oh, thank God! Thank God!"

John Southwell listened like a man in a dream. The news had stunned him, bewildered him; a new light shone in his eyes; he was altogether changed.

"Let me read it for myself, Martha," he cried. "Yes, it's true. It's come from Neuve Chapelle. It's, it's—— Why, Jack will have to come home! He'll have to receive his honour at the hands of the King! He'll—— Oh my wife! May God forgive me for all the hard things I've said about him; for the way I've treated him! You were right, Martha, always right," and then he kissed the cheeks that were streaming with happy tears.

"When will he come home, I wonder?" sobbed the mother. "I must have his room got ready! Oh, John, we must give him a great welcome! And—and—what's that?"

The door opened and a tall figure in khaki appeared in the room. The young officer was lean, and bore the marks of hardship, while his left arm was in a sling; but his eyes shone brightly.

"Mother! Dad!" was all he said.

□   □

"Why didn't you let us know where you were? what you were doing?" cried John Southwell at length. He seemed to have forgotten the past.

Jack hesitated a few seconds before replying.

"Because I determined not to, until you had ceased to be ashamed of me," was his answer. "I wanted to prove to you that——"

"There, there, my boy," interrupted the father, "not another word. It was I who was in the wrong. I did not—God forgive me—understand you. I wanted you to be shaped according to the mould I had decided on, and, and— But forgive me, my son. God only knows how proud I am of you now."

He left the room as he spoke, and did not return for some time.

"You are going to stay home for a long time—aren't you?" asked the mother eagerly.

"Until my arm is better, anyhow," replied Jack. "No, don't be anxious; it's going on all right."

"You must get some new clothes, Jack," said Mrs. Southwell.

There was a twinkle in Jack's eyes as he answered her. "Yes, I must. At any rate, I must have some more braid on my tunic."

"You don't mean that you are to be promoted?"

"The Colonel is no end of a sport," replied Jack. "He has recommended me for a Captaincy. I say, mother"—and Jack blushed as he spoke—"you don't mind if I go out for a few minutes, do you? I won't be long."

"You are sure you won't be long, Jack?"

"Only a few minutes, mother, only——"

"I don't think you'll find Mary Edgecumbe in, Jack," said John Southwell, and he laughed like a boy.

"What do you mean, Dad?"

"I mean that telephones are very useful things. If I mistake not, I hear my old friend George Edgecumbe in the hall. And isn't that Mary's voice?"

Mr. George Edgecumbe came into the room at once, but Jack and Mary Edgecumbe remained in the hall a long time together.

THE
FAIRY POODLE
By Leonard Merrick
Painting and Drawings by
Edmund Blampied

THEY were called the " Two Children " because they were so unprac-tical : even in bohemia, where practicality is the last virtue to flourish, their improvidence was surprising ; but really they were not children at all—they had been married for three years, though to watch their billing and cooing you would have supposed them to be bride and bridegroom.

Julien and Juliette had fallen in love and run to the Mairie as joyously as if chateaubriands were to be gathered from the boughs in the Jardin des Buttes-Chaumont ; and since then their home had been the studio under the slates, where they were often penniless. Indeed, if it had not been for the intermittent mercies of Madame Cochard, the concierge, they would have starved under the slates.

However, they were sure that the pictures which Julien painted would some day make him celebrated, and that the fairy tales which Juliette weaved would some day be as famous as Hans Andersen's. So they laughed, and painted and scribbled, and spent their money on bonbons instead of saving it for bread ; and when they had no dinner, they would kiss each other, and say, " There's a good time coming " ; and they were called the " Two Children," as you know.

But even the patience of Madame Cochard was taxed when Juliette brought back the poodle.

She found him—a strayed, muddy, unhappy little poodle— in the Rue de Rivoli one wet afternoon in November ; and what more natural than that she should immediately bear him home, and propose to give him a bath, and adopt him ? It was the most natural thing in the world, since she was Juliette ; yet this Madame Cochard, who objected to a dog on her stairs as violently as if it were a tiger, was furious.

" Is it not enough," she cried, " that you are the worst tenants in the house, you two—that you are always behindhand with your rent, and that I must fill your mouths out of my own purse ? Is a concierge an Angel from Heaven, do you think, that you expect her to provide also for lost dogs ? "

" Dear, kind Madame Cochard," cooed Juliette, " you will learn to love the little creature as if it were your own child ! See how trust-fully he regards you ! "

91

"It is a fact," added Julien; "he seems to take to her already! It is astonishing how quickly a dog recognises a good heart."

"Good heart or not," exclaimed the concierge, "it is to be understood that I do not consent to this outrage. The poodle shall not remain!"

"Be discreet," urged Juliette—"I entreat you to be discreet, for your own sake: if you must have the whole truth, he is a fairy poodle!"

"What do you say?" ejaculated Madame Cochard.

"He is a fairy poodle, and if we treat him ungenerously we shall suffer. Remember the history of the Lodgers, the Concierge, and the Pug!"

"I have never heard of such a history," returned Madame Cochard; "and I do not believe that there ever was one."

"She has never heard the history of the Lodgers, the Concierge, and the Pug!" cried Juliette. "Oh, then listen, madame! Once upon a time there were two lodgers, a young man and his wife, and they were so poor that often they depended on the tenderness of the concierge to supply them with a dinner."

"Did they also throw away their good money on bonbons and flowers?" asked Madame Cochard, trying her utmost to look severe.

"It is possible," admitted Juliette, who was perched on the table with the dirty little animal in her lap, "for though they are our hero and heroine, I cannot pretend that they were very wise. Well, this concierge, who suffered badly from lumbago and stairs, had sometimes a bit of temper, so you may figure to yourself what a fuss she raised when the poor lodgers brought home a friendless pug to add to their embarrassments. However——"

" There is no ' however,' " persisted Madame Cochard ; " she raises a fuss, and that is all about it ! "

" Pardon, dear madame,' put in Julien, " you confuse the cases ; we are now concerned with the veracious history of the pug, not the uncertain future of the poodle."

" Quite so," said Juliette. " She raised a terrible fuss and declared that the pug should go, but finally she melted to it and made it welcome. And then what do you suppose happened ? Why, it turned out to be an enchanted prince, who rewarded them all with wealth and happiness. The young man's pictures were immediately accepted by the Salon— did I mention that he was an artist ? The young woman's stories— did I tell you that she wrote stories ?—became so much the fashion that her head swam with joy ; and the concierge—the dear, kind concierge—was changed into a beautiful princess, and never had to walk up any stairs again as long as she lived. Thus we see that one should never forbid lodgers to adopt a dog ! "

" Thus we see that they do well to call you a pair of ' children ' ! " replied Madame Cochard—" that is what we see ! Well, well, keep the dog, since you are so much bent on it ; only I warn you that if it gives me trouble, it will be sausages in no time ! I advise you to wash it without delay, for a more deplorable little beast I never saw."

Julien and Juliette set to work with delight, and after he was bathed and dry the alteration in the dog was quite astonishing.

Although he did not precisely turn into a prince, he turned into a poodle of the most fashionable aspect. Obviously an aristocrat among poodles, a poodle of high estate.

The metamorphosis was so striking that a new fear assailed his rescuers, the fear that it might be dishonest of them to retain him— probably some great lady was disconsolate at his loss !

Sure enough ! A few days later, when Sanquereau called upon them, he said :

" By the way, did I not hear that you had found a poodle, my children ? Doubtless it is the poodle for which they advertise. See ! " And he produced a copy of a journal in which " a handsome reward " was promised for the restoration of an animal which resembled their protégé to a tuft.

The description was too accurate for the Children to deceive themselves, and that afternoon Juliette carried the dog to a magnificent house which was nothing less than the residence of the Comtesse de Grand Ecusson.

She was left standing in a noble hall while a flunkey bore the dog away.

Then another flunkey bade her follow him upstairs ; and in a salon which was finer than anything that Juliette had ever met with

outside the pages of a novel, the Countess was reclining on a couch with the poodle in her arms.

" I am so grateful to you for the recovery of my darling," said the great lady; " my distress has been insupportable. Ah, naughty, naughty Racine ! "

She made a pretence of chastising the poodle on the nose.

" I can understand it, madame," said Juliette, much embarrassed.

" Where did you find him ? And has he been well fed, well taken care of ? I hope he has not been sleeping in a draught ? "

" Oh, indeed, madame, he has been nourished like a beloved child. Doubtless, not so delicately as with madame But——"

" It was most kind of you," said the lady. " I count myself blessed that my little Racine fell into such good hands. Now as to the reward : what sum would you think sufficient ? "

Juliette looked shy. " I thank you, madame, but we could not accept anything," she faltered.

" What ! " exclaimed the Countess, raising her eyebrows in surprise, " you cannot accept anything ? How is that ? "

" Well," said Juliette, " it would be base to accept money for a simple act of honesty. It is true that we did not wish to part with the dog—we had grown to love him—but, as to our receiving payment for giving him up, that is impossible."

The Countess laughed merrily. " What a funny child you are ! And who are ' we ' ?—you and your parents ? "

" Oh no," said Juliette ; " my parents are in heaven, madame ; but I am married."

" Your husband must be in heaven too ! " said the Countess, who was a charming woman.

" Ah," demurred Juliette, " but although I have a warm heart, I have also a healthy appetite, and he is not rich ; he is a painter."

" I must go to see his pictures some day," replied the Comtesse de Grand Ecusson. " Give me the address—and believe that I am extremely grateful to you ! "

It need not be said that Juliette skipped home on air after this interview.

The hint of such patronage opened the gates of paradise to her, and the prospect was equally dazzling to Julien.

For fully a week they talked of nothing but a visit from the Comtesse de Grand Ecusson, having no suspicion that fine ladies often forgot their pretty promises as quickly as they made them.

And the week, and a fortnight, and a month passed, and at last the expectation faded ; they ceased to indulge their fancies of a carriage-and-pair dashing into the street with a Lady Bountiful.

And what was much more serious, Madame Cochard ceased to indulge their follies. The truth was that she had never pardoned the girl for refusing to accept the proffered reward ; the delicacy that prompted the refusal was beyond her comprehension, and now that the pair were in arrears with their rent again, she put no bridle on her tongue.

"It appears to me that it would have been more honourable to accept money for a poodle than to owe money to a landlord," she grunted. "It must be perfectly understood that if the sum is not forthcoming on the first of January, you will have to get out. I have received my instructions, and I shall obey them. On the first day of January, my children, you pay, or you go ! Le bon Dieu alone knows what will become of you, but that is no affair of mine. I expect you will die like the babes in the wood, for you are no more fit to make a living than a cow is fit to fly."

"Dear Madame Cochard," they answered, peacefully, "why distress yourself about us ? The first of January is more than a week distant ; in a week we may sell a picture, or some fairy tales—in a week many things may happen ! "

And they sunned themselves on the Boulevard the same afternoon with as much serenity as if they had been millionaires.

Nevertheless, they did not sell a picture or some fairy tales in the week that followed—and the first of January dawned with relentless punctuality, as we all remember.

In the early morning, when Madame Cochard made her ascent to the attic—her arms folded inexorably, the glare of a creditor in her eye—she found that Juliette had already been out. (If you can believe me, she had been out to waste her last two francs on an absurd tie for Julien !)

"Eh bien," demanded the concierge sternly, "where is your husband ? I am here, as arranged, for the rent : no doubt he has it ready on the mantelpiece for me ? "

"He is not in," answered Juliette coaxingly, "and I am sorry to say we have had disappointments. The fact is there is something wrong in the construction of a story of which I had immense hopes— it needs letting out at the waist, and a tuck put in at the hem. When I have made the alterations, I am sure it will fit some journal elegantly."

"All this passes forbearance !" exclaimed Madame Cochard. "Well, you have thoroughly understood, and all is said—you will vacate your lodging by

evening! So much grace I give you; but at six o'clock you depart promptly, or you will be ejected! And do not reckon on me to send any meal up here during the day, for you will not get so much as a crust. What is it that you have been buying there?"

"It is a little gift for Julien; I rose early to choose it before he woke, and surprise him; but when I returned he was out."

"A gift?" cried the concierge. "You have no money to buy food, and you buy a gift for your husband! What for?"

"What for?" repeated Juliette wonderingly. "Why, because it is New Year's Day! And that reminds me—I wish you the compliments of the season, madame; may you enjoy many happy years!"

"Kind words pay no bills," snapped the concierge. "I have been lenient far too long—I have my own reputation to consider with the landlord. By six o'clock, bear in mind!"

And then, to complete her resentment, what should happen but that Julien entered bearing a bouquet!

To see Julien present Juliette with the roses, and to watch Juliette enchant Julien with the preposterous tie, was as charming a little comedy of improvidence as you would be likely to meet with in a lifetime.

"Mon Dieu!" gasped Madame Cochard, purple with indignation, "it is indeed well that you are leaving here, monsieur—a madhouse is the fitting address for you! You have nothing to eat, and you buy roses for your wife? What for?"

"What for?" echoed Julien, astonished. "Why, because it is New Year's Day! And I take the opportunity to wish you the compliments of the season, madame—may your future be as bright as Juliette's eyes!"

"By six o'clock—" reiterated the concierge, who was so exasperated that she could barely articulate—"by six o'clock you will be out of the place!"

And to relieve her feelings she slammed the door with such violence that half a dozen canvases fell to the floor.

"Well, this is a nice thing," remarked Julien, when she had gone. "It looks to me, mignonne, as if we shall sleep in the Bois, with the moon for an eiderdown!"

"At least you shall have a comfy pillow, sweetheart," cried Juliette, drawing his head to her breast.

"My angel, there is none so soft in the Elysée! And as we have nothing for déjeuner in the cupboard, I propose that we breakfast now on kisses."

THE FAIRY POODLE.

A visitor! Madame la Comtesse de Grand Ecusson!

From a painting by E. Blampied

"Ah, Julien!" whispered the girl, as she folded him in her arms.

"Ah, Juliette!" It was as if they had been married that morning.

"And yet," continued the young man, releasing her at last, "to own the truth, your kisses are not satisfying as a menu; they are the choicest of hors d'œuvres—they leave one hungry for more!"

They were still making love when Sanquereau burst in to wish them a Happy New Year.

"How goes it, my children?" he cried. "You look like a honeymoon, I swear! Am I in the way, or may I breakfast with you?"

"You are not in the way, mon vieux," returned Julien; "but I shall not invite you to breakfast with me, because my repast consists of Juliette's lips."

"Mon Dieu!" said Sanquereau. "So you are broke? Well, in my chequered career I have breakfasted on much worse fare than yours."

At this reply, Juliette blushed with all the bashfulness of a bride, and Julien endeavoured to assume the air of a man of the world.

"Tell me," he said: "we are in difficulties about the rent—have you by chance a louis that you could lend me?"

Sanquereau turned out his pockets, like the good fellow he was, but he could produce no more than a sou.

"What a bother!" he cried: "I would lend you a louis if I had it as readily as a cigarette paper, but you see how I am situated. On my honour, it rends my heart to have to refuse."

"You are a gallant comrade!" said Julien, much touched. "Come back and sup with us this evening, and we will open the New Year with a festivity!"

"Hein? But there will be no supper," faltered Juliette.

"That's true," said Julien; "there will be no supper—I was forgetting. Still—who knows? There is plenty of time; I shall have an idea. Perhaps I may be able to borrow something from Tricotrin."

"I shall be enchanted," responded Sanquereau; "depend on my arrival! If I am not mistaken, I recognise Tricotrin's voice on the stairs."

His ears had not deceived him; Tricotrin appeared with Pitou at this very moment.

8

"Greeting, my children!" they cried. "How wags the world? May the New Year bring you laurels and lucre!"

"To you also, dear Gustave and Nicolas," cried 'the Children.' "May your poems and your music ignite the Seine, and may Sanquereau rise to eminence and make statues of you both!"

"In the meantime," added Sanquereau, "can either of you put your hands on a few francs? There is a fine opening for them here!"

"A difference of opinion exists between ourselves and the land-lord," Julien explained: "we consider that he should wait for his rent, and he holds a different view. If you could lend us fifteen francs, we might effect a compromise."

The poet and the composer displayed the lining of their pockets as freely as the sculptor had done, but their capital proved to be a sou less than his own. Tears sprang to their eyes as they confessed their inability to be of use. "We are in despair," they groaned.

"My good, kind friends!" exclaimed Julien, "your sympathy is a noble gift in itself! Join us in a little supper this evening in celebra-tion of the date."

"We shall be delighted," declared Tricotrin and Pitou.

"But—but——" stammered Juliette again, "where is it to come from, this supper?—and where shall we be by supper-time?"

"Well, our address is on the lap of the gods," admitted Julien, "but while there is life there is hope. Possibly I may obtain a loan from Lajeunie."

Not many minutes had passed before Lajeunie also paid a visit to the attic. "Aha," cried the unsuccessful novelist, as he perceived the company, "well met! My children, my brothers, may your rewards equal your deserts this year—may France do honour to your genius!"

"And may Lajeunie be crowned the new Balzac," shouted the assembly; "may his abode be in the Champs Elysées, and his name in the mouth of all the world!"

But, extraordinary as it appears, Lajeunie proved to be as impe-cunious as the rest there; and he was so much distressed that Julien, deeply moved, said:

"Come back to supper, Lajeunie; we will drink toasts to the Muses!"

And now there were four guests invited to the impracticable supper, and when the Children were left alone they clapped their hands at the prospect.

"How merry we shall be!" Julien exclaimed; "and awhile ago we talked of passing the night in the Bois! It only shows you that one can never tell what an hour may bring forth."

"Yes, yes," assented Juliette blithely; "and as for the supper——"

"We shall not require it till nine o'clock at the earliest."

"And now it is no more than midday! Why, there is an eternity for things to arrange themselves!"

"Just so! The sky may rain truffles in such an interval," said the painter. And they drew their chairs closer to the fire, and pretended to each other they were not hungry.

The hours crept past, and the sunshine waned, and snow began to flutter over Paris. But no truffles fell. By degrees the fire burnt low, and died. To beg for more fuel was impossible, and Juliette shivered a little.

"You are cold, sweetheart," sighed Julien. "I will fetch a blanket from the bed and wrap you in it."

"No," she murmured, "wrap me in your arms—it will be better."

Darker and darker grew the garret, and faster and faster fell the snow.

"I have a fancy," said Juliette, breaking a long silence, "that it is the hour in which a fairy should appear to us. Let us look to see if she is coming!"

They peered from the window, but in the twilight no fairy was to be discerned—only an old clo' man was visible, trudging on his round.

"I declare," cried Julien, "he is the next best thing to your fairy! I will sell my summer suit and my velvet jacket! What do I want of a velvet jacket? Coffee and eggs will be much more cheerful."

"And I," vowed Juliette, "can spare my best hat easily—indeed, it is an encumbrance! If we make Madame Cochard a small peace-offering she may allow us to remain until the morning."

"What a grand idea! We shall provide ourselves with a night's shelter and the means to entertain our friends as well. Hasten to collect our wardrobe, mignonette, while I crack my throat to make him hear.—Hé, hé!"

At the repeated cries the old clo' man lifted his gaze to the fifth-floor window at last, and in a few minutes Julien and Juliette were kneeling on the boards above a pile of garments, which they raised one by one for his inspection.

"Regard, monsieur," said Julien, "this elegant summer suit! It is almost as good as new! I begin to hesitate to part with it. What shall we say for this elegant summer suit?"

The dealer fingered it disdainfully. "Show me boots," he suggested; "we can do business in boots."

"Alas!" replied Julien, "the only boots that I possess are on my feet. We will again admire the suit. What do you estimate it at—ten francs?"

"Are you insane? are you a lunatic?" returned the dealer. "To a reckless man it might be worth ten sous. Let us talk of boots!"

"I cannot go barefooted," expostulated Julien. "Juliette, my Heart, do you happen to possess a second pair of boots?"

Juliette shook her head forlornly. "But I have a hat with daisies

in it," she said. "Observe, monsieur, the delicate tints of the buds! How like to nature, how exquisite they are! They make one dream of courtship in the woods. I will take five francs for it!"

"From me I swear you will not take them!" said the old clo' man. "Boots," he pleaded; "for the love of God, boots!"

"What a passion for boots you have!" moaned the unhappy painter; "they obsess you, they warp your judgment! Can you think of nothing in the world but boots? Look, we come to the gem of the exhibition—a velvet jacket! A jacket like this confers an air of greatness; one could not feel the pinch of poverty in such a jacket. It is, I confess, a little white at the elbows, but such high lights are very effective. And observe the texture—as soft as a darling's cheek!"

The other turned it about with indifferent hands, and the Children began to realize that he would prove no substitute for a fairy after all. Then, while they watched him with sinking hearts, the door was suddenly opened, and the concierge tottered on the threshold.

"Monsieur!—madame!" she panted, with such respect that they stared at each other.

"Eh bien?"

"A visitor!" She leant against the wall, overwhelmed.

"Who is it?"

"Madame la Comtesse de Grand Ecusson!"

Actually! The Countess had kept her word after all, and now she rustled in, before the old clo' man could be banished.

White as a virgin canvas, Julien staggered forward to receive her, a pair of trousers, which he was too agitated to remember, dangling under his arm.

"Madame, this honour!" he stammered; and, making a piteous effort to disguise his beggary, "One's wardrobe accumulates so that, really, in a small ménage, one has no room to——"

"I have suffered from the inconvenience myself, monsieur," said the Countess graciously. "Your charming wife was so kind as to invite me to view your work; and see—my little Racine has come to wish his preservers a Happy New Year!"

And on the honour of a historian, he brought one! Before they left she had given a commission for his portrait at a thousand francs, and purchased two landscapes, for which a thousand francs more would be paid on the morrow.

When Sanquereau and Lajeunie and Tricotrin and Pitou arrived, expecting the worst, they were amazed to discover the Children valsing round the attic to the music of their own voices.

What *hurras* rang out when the explanation was forthcoming; what loans were promised to the guests, and what a gay quadrille was danced!

It was not until the last figure had concluded that Julien and Juliette recognised that, although they would be wealthy in the morning, they were still penniless that night.

"Hélas! but we have no supper after all," groaned Julien.

"Pardon, it is here, monsieur!" shouted Madame Cochard, who at this moment entered behind a kingly feast. "*Comment*, shall the artist honoured by Madame la Comtesse de Grand Ecusson have no supper? Pot-au-feu, monsieur; leg of mutton, monsieur; little tarts, monsieur; dessert, monsieur; and for each person a bottle of good wine!"

And the justice that was done to it, and the laughter that pealed under the slates! The Children didn't forget that it was all due to the dog. Juliette raised her glass radiantly:

"Gentlemen!" she cried, "I ask you to drink to the Fairy Poodle!"

THE
PORTRAIT OF A LADY
By Jerome K. Jerome
Drawings by
Gordon Browne, R.I.

My work pressed upon me, but the louder it challenged me—such is the heart of the timid fighter—the less stomach I felt for the contest. I wrestled with it in my study, only to be driven to my books. I walked out to meet it in the streets, only to seek shelter from it in music-hall or theatre. Thereupon it waxed importunate and overbearing, till the shadow of it darkened all my doings. The thought of it sat beside me at the table, and spoilt my appetite. The memory of it followed me abroad, and stood between me and my friends, so that all talk died upon my lips, and I moved among men as one ghost-ridden.

Then the throbbing town, with its thousand distracting voices, grew maddening to me. I felt the need of converse with solitude, that master and teacher of all the arts, and I bethought me of the Yorkshire Wolds, where a man may walk all day, meeting no human creature, hearing no voice but the curlew's cry; where, lying prone upon the sweet grass, he may feel the pulsation of the earth, travelling its eleven hundred miles a minute through the æther. So one morning I bundled many things, some needful, more needless, into a bag, hurrying lest somebody or something should happen to stay me; and that night I lay in a small northern town, that stands upon the borders of smokedom at the gate of the great moors; and at seven the next morning I took my seat beside a one-eyed carrier, behind an ancient piebald mare. The one-eyed carrier cracked his whip, the piebald horse jogged forward; the nineteenth century, with its turmoil, fell away behind us; the distant hills, creeping nearer, swallowed us up, and we became but a moving speck upon the face of the quiet earth.

Late in the afternoon we arrived at a village, the memory of which had been growing in my mind. It lies in the triangle formed by the sloping walls of three great fells; and not even the telegraph wire has reached it yet, to murmur to it whispers of the restless world—or had not at the time of which I write. Naught disturbs it save, once a day, the one-eyed carrier—if he and his piebald mare have not yet laid their ancient bones to rest—who, passing through, leaves a few

letters and parcels to be called for by the people of the scattered hill-farms round about. It is the meeting-place of two noisy brooks. Through the sleepy days and the hushed nights, one hears them ever chattering to themselves as children playing alone some game of make-believe. Coming from their far-off homes among the hills, they mingle their waters here, and journey on in company, and then their converse is more serious, as becomes those who have joined hands and are moving onward towards life together. Later they reach sad, weary towns, black beneath a never-lifted pall of smoke, where day and night the clang of iron drowns all human voices, where the children play with ashes, where the men and women have dull, patient faces; and so, muddy and stained, to the deep sea that ceaselessly calls to them. Here, however, their waters are fresh and clear, and their passing makes the only stir that the valley has ever known. Surely, of all peaceful places, this was the one where a tired worker might find strength.

My one-eyed friend had suggested I should seek lodgings at the house of one Mistress Cholmondley, a widow lady, who resided with her only daughter in the whitewashed cottage that is the last house in the village, if you take the road that leads over Coll Fell.

"Tha' can see th' house from here, by reason o' its standing so high above t'others," said the carrier, pointing with his whip. "It's theer or nowhere, aw'm thinking, for folks don't often coom seeking lodgings in these parts."

The tiny dwelling, half-smothered in June roses, looked idyllic; and, after a lunch of bread and cheese at the little inn, I made my way to it by the path that passes through the churchyard. I had conjured up the vision of a stout, pleasant, comfort-radiating woman, assisted by some bright, fresh girl, whose rosy cheeks and sunburnt hands would help me banish from my mind all clogging recollections of the town; and, hopeful, I pushed back the half-opened door and entered.

The cottage was furnished with a taste that surprised me, but in themselves my hosts disappointed me. My bustling, comely house-wife turned out a wizened, blear-eyed dame. All day long she dozed in her big chair, or crouched with shrivelled hands spread out before the fire. My dream of winsome maidenhood vanished before the reality of a weary-looking, sharp-featured woman of between forty and fifty. Perhaps there had been a time when the listless eyes had sparkled with roguish merriment, when the shrivelled, tight-drawn lips had pouted temptingly; but spinsterhood does not sweeten the juices of a woman, and strong country air, though, like old ale, it is good when taken occasionally, dulls the brain if lived upon. A narrow, uninteresting woman I found her; troubled with a shyness that sat ludicrously upon her age, and that yet failed to save her from the landlady's customary failing of loquacity concerning "better days," together with an irritating, if harmless, affectation of youthfulness.

All other details were, however, most satisfactory; and at the window commanding the road that leads through the valley towards the distant world, I settled down to face my work.

But the spirit of industry, once driven forth, returns with coy steps. I wrote for perhaps an hour; and then, throwing down my halting pen, I looked about the room, seeking distraction. A Chippendale bookcase stood against the wall, and I strolled over to it. The key was in the lock, and opening its glass doors, I examined the well-filled shelves. They held a curious collection : miscellanies with quaint, glazed bindings; novels, and poems, whose authors I had never heard of; old magazines long dead, their very names forgotten; "keepsakes" and annuals, redolent of an age of vastly pretty sentiments and lavender-coloured silks. On the top shelf, however, was a volume of Keats, wedged between a number of the *Evangelical Rambler* and Young's *Night Thoughts*, and, standing on tip-toe, I sought to draw it from its place.

The book was jambed so tightly that my efforts brought two or three others tumbling about me, covering me with a cloud of fine dust; and to my feet there fell, with a rattle of glass and metal, a small miniature painting, framed in black wood.

I picked it up, and, taking it to the window, examined it. It was the picture of a young girl, dressed in the fashion of thirty years ago —I mean thirty years ago then. I fear it must be nearer fifty, speaking as from now—when our grandmothers wore corkscrew curls, and low-cut bodices that one wonders how they kept from slipping down. The face was beautiful, not merely with the conventional beauty of tiresome regularity and impossible colouring such as one finds in all miniatures, but with soul behind the soft deep eyes. As I gazed, the sweet lips seemed to laugh at me, and yet there lurked a sadness in the smile, as though the artist, in some rare moment, had seen the coming shadow of life across the sunshine of the face. Even my small knowledge of Art told me that the work was clever, and I wondered why it should have lain so long neglected, when as a mere ornament it was valuable. It must have been placed in the book-case years ago by some one, and forgotten.

I replaced it among its dusty companions, and sat down once more to my work. But between me and the fading light came the face of the miniature, and would not be banished. Wherever I turned it looked out at me from the shadows. I am not naturally fanciful, and the work I was engaged upon, the writing of a farcical comedy, was not of the kind to excite the dreamy side of a man's nature. I grew angry with myself, and made a further effort to fix my mind upon the paper in front of me. But my thoughts refused to return from their wanderings. Once, glancing back over my shoulder, I could have sworn I saw the original of the picture sitting in the big chintz-covered chair in the far corner. It was dressed in a faded lilac frock, trimmed with some old lace, and I could not help noticing the beauty of the folded hands, though in the portrait only the head and shoulders had been drawn.

Next morning I had forgotten the incident, but with the lighting of the lamp the memory of it awoke within me, and my interest grew so strong that again I took the miniature from its hiding-place and looked at it.

And then the knowledge suddenly came to me that I knew the face. Where had I seen her, and when? I had met her and spoken to her. The picture smiled at me, as if rallying me on my forgetfulness. I put it back upon its shelf, and sat racking my brains, trying to recollect: we had met somewhere—in the country—a long time ago, and had talked of commonplace things. To the vision of her clung the scent of roses and the murmuring voices of haymakers. Why had I never seen her again? Why had she passed so completely out of my mind?

My landlady entered to lay my supper, and I questioned her, assuming a careless tone. Reason with or laugh at myself as I would, this shadowy memory was becoming a romance to me. It was as though I were talking of some loved, dead friend, even to speak of whom to commonplace people was a sacrilege. I did not want the woman to question me in return.

"Oh, yes," answered my landlady. Ladies had often lodged with her. Sometimes people stayed the whole summer, wandering about the woods and fells, but to her thinking the great hills were lonesome. Some of her lodgers had been young ladies, but she could not remember any of them having impressed her with their beauty. But then it was said women were never judges of other women. They had come and gone. Few had ever returned; and fresh faces drove out the old.

"You have been letting lodgings for a long time?" I asked. "I suppose it could be fifteen—twenty years ago that strangers to you lived in this room?"

"Longer than that," she said quietly, dropping for the moment all affectation. "We came here from the farm when my father died.

He had had losses, and there was but little left. That is twenty-seven years ago now."

I hastened to close the conversation, fearing long-winded recollections of " better days." I have heard such so often from one landlady and another. I had not learnt much. Who was the original of the miniature, how it came to be lying forgotten in the dusty bookcase were still mysteries; and with a strange perversity I could not have explained to myself, I shrank from putting a direct question.

So two days more passed by. My work took gradually a firmer grip upon my mind, and the face of the miniature visited me less often. But in the evening of the third day, which was a Sunday, a curious thing happened.

I was returning from a stroll, and dusk was falling as I reached the cottage. I had been thinking of my farce, and I was laughing to myself at a situation that seemed to me comical, when, passing the window of my room, I saw looking out the sweet, fair face that had become so familiar to me. It stood close to the latticed panes—a slim, girlish figure, clad in the old-fashioned lilac-coloured frock in which I had imagined it on the first night of my arrival, the beautiful hands clasped across the breast, as then they had been folded on the lap. Her eyes were gazing down the road that passes through the village and goes south; but they seemed to be dreaming, not seeing, and the sadness in them struck upon one almost as a cry. I was close to the window, but the hedge screened me, and I remained watching until, after a minute I suppose, though it appeared longer, the figure drew back into the darkness of the room and disappeared.

I entered, but the room was empty. I called, but no one answered. The uncomfortable suggestion took hold of me that I must be growing a little crazy. All that had gone before I could explain to myself as a mere train of thought, but this time it had come to me suddenly —uninvited, while my thoughts had been busy elsewhere. This thing had appeared not to my brain but to my senses. I am not a believer in ghosts, but I am in the hallucinations of a weak mind, and my own explanation was in consequence not very satisfactory to myself.

I tried to dismiss the incident, but it would not leave me; and later that same evening something else occurred that fixed it still clearer in my thoughts. I had taken out two or three books at random with which to amuse myself, and turning over the leaves of one of them, a volume of verses by some obscure poet, I found its sentimental passages much scored and commented upon in pencil, as was common fifty years ago—as may be common now, for your Fleet Street cynic has not altered the world and its ways to quite the extent that he imagines.

One poem in particular had evidently appealed greatly to the reader's sympathies. It was the old, old story of the gallant who woos and rides away, leaving the maiden to weep. The poetry was poor, and at another time its conventionality would have excited only my ridicule. But, reading it in conjunction with the quaint, naïve notes scattered about its margins, I felt no inclination to jeer. These hackneyed stories that we laugh at are deep profundities to the many who find in them some shadow of their own sorrows, and she—for it was a woman's handwriting—to whom this book belonged had loved its trite verses, because in them she had read her own heart. This, I told myself, was her story also; a common enough story in life as in literature, but novel to those who live it.

There was no reason for my connecting her with the original of the miniature, except perhaps a subtle relationship between the thin nervous handwriting and the mobile features; yet I felt instinctively they were one and the same, and that I was tracing, link by link, the history of my forgotten friend.

I felt urged to probe further, and next morning, while my landlady was clearing away my breakfast things, I fenced round the subject once again.

"By the way," I said, "while I think of it, if I leave any books or papers here behind me, send them on at once. I have a knack of doing that sort of thing. I suppose," I added, "your lodgers often do leave some of their belongings behind them?"

It sounded to myself a clumsy ruse. I wondered if she would suspect what was behind it.

"Not often," she answered; "never, that I can remember, except in the case of one poor lady, who died here."

I glanced up quickly. "In this room?" I asked.

My landlady seemed troubled at my tone. "Well, not exactly in this very room. We carried her upstairs, but she died immediately. She was dying when she came here. I should not have taken her in had I known. So many people are prejudiced against a house where death has occurred, as if there were anywhere it had not. It was not quite fair to us."

I did not speak for a while, and the rattle of the plates and knives continued undisturbed.

"What did she leave here?" I asked at length.

"Oh, just a few books and photographs, and such-like small things that people bring with them to lodgings," was the reply. "Her people promised to send for them, but they never did, and I suppose I forgot them. They were not of any value."

The woman turned as she was leaving the room. "It won't drive you away, sir, I hope, what I have told you?" she said. "It all happened a long while ago."

"Of course not," I answered. "It interested me, that was all." And the woman went out, closing the door behind her.

So here was the explanation, if I chose to accept it. I sat long that morning, wondering to myself whether things I had learnt to laugh at could be after all realities. And a day or two afterwards I made a discovery that confirmed all my vague surmises.

Rummaging through this same dusty book-case, I found in one of the ill-fitting drawers, beneath a heap of torn and tumbled books, a diary, belonging to the fifties, stuffed with many letters and shapeless flowers, pressed between stained pages; and there—for the writer of stories, tempted by human documents, is weak—in faded ink, brown and withered like the flowers, I read the story I already knew.

Such a very old story it was, and so conventional. He was an artist, —was ever story of this type written where the hero was not an artist? They had been children together, loving each other without knowing it, till one day it was revealed to them. Here is the entry:—

"May 18th. I do not know what to say, or how to begin. Chris. loves me. I have been praying to God to make me worthy of him, and dancing round the room in my bare feet for fear of waking them below. He kissed my hands and clasped them round his neck, saying they were beautiful as the hands of a goddess, and he knelt and kissed them again. I am holding them before me and kissing them myself. I am glad they are so beautiful. O God, why are you so good to me? Help me to be a true wife to him. Help me that I may never give him an instant's pain! Oh, that I had more power of loving, that I might love him better,"—and thus foolish thoughts for many pages, but foolish thoughts of the kind that has kept this worn old world, hanging for so many ages in space, from turning sour.

Later, in February, there is another entry that carries on the story:—

"Chris. left this morning. He put a little packet into my hands at the last moment, saying it was the most precious thing he possessed, and that when I looked at it I was to think of him who loved it. Of course I guessed what it was, but I did not open it till I was alone in my room. It is the picture of myself that he has been so secret about, but oh, so beautiful! I wonder if I am really as beautiful as this. But I wish he had not made me look so sad. I am kissing the little lips. I love them, because he loved to kiss them. O sweetheart! it will be long before you kiss them again. Of course, it was right for him to go, and I am glad he has been able to manage it. He could not study properly in this quiet country place, and now he will be able to go to Paris and Rome, and he will be great. Even the stupid people here see how clever he is. But, oh, it will be so long before I see him again—my love! my king!"

With each letter that comes from him, similar foolish rhapsodies are written down; but these letters of his, I gather, as I turn the pages, grow after a while colder and fewer, and a chill fear that dare not be penned creeps in among the words.

"March 12th. Six weeks and no letter from Chris.; and oh dear! I am so hungry for one, for the last I have almost kissed to pieces. I suppose he will write more often when he gets to London. He is working hard, I know, and it is selfish of me to expect him to write more often; but I would sit up all night for a week rather than miss writing to him. I suppose men are not like that. O God, help me— help me, whatever happens! How foolish I am to-night! He was always careless. I will punish him for it when he comes back, but not very much." Truly enough a conventional story.

Letters do come from him after that, but apparently they are less and less satisfactory, for the diary grows angry and bitter, and the faded writing is blotted at times with tears. Then towards the end of another year there comes this entry, written in a hand of strange neatness and precision :—

"It is all over now. I am glad it is finished. I have written to him, giving him up. I have told him I have ceased to care for him,

and that it is better we should both be free. It is best that way. He would have had to ask me to release him, and that would have given him pain. He was always gentle. Now he will be able to marry her with an easy conscience, and he need never know what I have suffered. She is more fitted for him than I am. I hope he will be happy. I think I have done the right thing."

A few lines follow, left blank, and then the writing is resumed, but in a stronger, more vehement hand.

"Why do I lie to myself? I hate her! I would kill her if I could. I hope she will make him wretched, and that he will come to hate her as I do, and that she will die! Why did I let them persuade me to send that lying letter? He will show it to her, and she will see through it and laugh at me. I could have held him to his promise; he could not have got out of it.

"What do I care about dignity, and womanliness, and right, and all the rest of the canting words! I want him. I want his kisses, and his arms about me. He is mine! He loved me once! I have only given him up because I thought it a fine thing to play the saint. It is only an acted lie. I would rather be evil, and he loved me. Why do I deceive myself? I want him. I care for nothing else at the bottom of my heart—his love, his kisses!" And towards the end: "My God, what am I saying? Have I no shame, no strength? O God, help me!"

And there the diary closes.

I looked among the letters, lying between the pages of the book. Most of them were signed simply "Chris." or "Christopher." But one gave his name in full, and it was a name I know well as that of a famous man, whose hand I have often shaken. I thought of his hard-featured, handsome wife, and of his great chill place, half house, half exhibition, in Kensington, filled constantly with its smart, chattering set, among whom he seemed always to be the uninvited guest; of his weary face and bitter tongue. And thinking thus, there rose up before me the sweet, sad face of the woman of the miniature, and, meeting her eyes as she smiled at me from out of the shadows, I looked at her my wonder.

I took the miniature from its shelf. There would be no harm now in learning her name. So I stood with it in my hand till a little later my landlady entered to lay the cloth.

"I tumbled this out of your book-case," I said, "in reaching down some books. It is some one I know—some one I have met, but I cannot think where. Do you know who it is?"

The woman took it from my hand, and a faint flush crossed her withered face. "I had lost it," she answered. "I never thought of looking there. It's a portrait of myself, painted years ago by a friend."

I looked from her to the miniature, as she stood among the shadows, with the lamplight falling on her face, and saw her perhaps for the first time. "How stupid of me!" I answered. "Yes, I see the likeness now."

VICTORY DAY

AN ANTICIPATION

By John Oxenham

Painting by

Eugène Hastain

Drawings by

Claude A. Shepperson, A.R.W.S.

As sure as God's in His Heaven,
As sure as He stands for Right,
As sure as the hun this wrong hath
    done,
So surely we win this fight !

Then !—
Then, the visioned eye shall see
The great and noble company,
That gathers there from land and sea,
From over-land and over-sea,
From under-land and under-sea,
To celebrate right royally
        The Day of Victory.

Not alone on that great day
Will the war-worn victors come,
    To meet our great glad " Welcome
      Home ! "
    And a whole world's deep " Well
      done ! "
    Not alone ! Not alone will they
      come,
    To the sound of the pipe and the
      drum ;
    They will come to their own
    With the pipe and the drum,
    With the merry merry tune
    Of the pipe and the drum ;—
    But — they — will — not — come—
      alone !

111

In their unseen myriads there,
Unperceived, but no less there,
In the vast of God's own air,
       They will come!—
With never a pipe or a drum,
All the flower of Christendom,
In a silence more majestic,—
They will come! They will come!
The unknown and the known,
To meet our deep " Well done! "
And the world-resounding thunders
Of our great glad " Welcome Home! "

With their faces all alight,
And their brave eyes shining bright,
From their glorious martyrdom,
       They will come!
They will once more all unite
With their comrades of the fight,
To share the world's delight
In the Victory of Right,
And the doom—the final doom—
The final, full, and everlasting doom
Of brutal Might,
       They will come!

At the world-convulsing boom
Of the treacherous Austrian gun,—
At the all-compelling " Come! "
Of that deadly signal-gun,—
They gauged the peril, and they came.
—Of many a race, and many a name,
But all ablaze with one white flame,
They tarried not to count the cost,
But came.
They came from many a clime and coast,—
The slim of limb, the dark of face,
They shouldered eager in the race
The sturdy giants of the frost,
And the stalwarts of the sun.—
Britons, Britons, Britons are they!
       Britons, every one!

It shall be their lifelong boast,
That they counted not the cost,

VICTORY DAY.

Those who lived, and those who died,
They were one in noble pride. . . .
Britons, Britons, Britons are they !—
Britons, every one !

From a painting by Eugène Hastain

But at the Mother-Country's call they came.
They came a wrong to right,
They came to end the blight
Of a vast ungodly might;
And by their gallant coming overcame.
Britons, Britons, Britons are they!
   Britons, every one!

It shall be their nobler boast,—
It shall spell their endless fame,—
That, regardless of the cost,
They won the world for Righteousness,
And cleansed it of its shame.
Britons, Britons, Britons, are they!
   Britons, every one!

And now,—again they come,
With merry pipe and drum,
Amid the storming cheers,
And the grateful-streaming tears,
Of this our great, glad, sorrowing Welcome-Home.
They shall every one be there,
On the earth or in the air,
From the land and from the sea,
And from under-land and sea,
Not a man shall missing be
From the past and present fighting-strength
Of that great company.
Those who lived, and those who died,
They were one in noble pride
Of desperate endeavour and of duty nobly done;
For their lives they risked and gave
Very Soul of Life to save,
And by their own great valour and the Grace of God they won.
Britons, Britons, Britons are they!—
   Britons, every one!

NORAH

By
Gilbert Parker

Drawings by
C. E. Brock

I

It was as fine a churchful as you ever clapt an eye on;
  Oh, the bells was ringin' gaily, and the sun was shinin' free;
There was singers, there was clargy—"Bless you both," says Father Tryon—
  They was weddin' Mary Callaghan and me.

There was gatherin' of women, there was hush upon the stairway,
  There was whisperin' and smilin', but it was no place for me;
A little ship was comin' into harbour through the fairway—
  It belongs to Mary Callaghan and me.

Shure, the longest day has endin', and the wildest storm has fallin'—
  There's a young gossoon in yander, and he sits upon my knee;
There's a churchful for the christenin'—do you hear the imp a-callin'?
  He's the pride of Mary Callaghan and me!

IT was a voice worth hearing, and the man was worth seeing, as, standing in a large paddock in front of a house, which for the prairie-country was a large one, he drove the colt he was breaking round a circle, at the end of a long leather rein. He had in his face the look of one who had lived life in more ways than one, and his shoulders had the straightness of one who had known the "'Shun!'" of the drill-sergeant, though he was over forty years of age. In this perfect sunlight, with the gold-brown stubble of the reaped land stretching for scores of miles away, he seemed the true representative of a life of energy and happiness. His face was ruddy, his eye bright; but his hat, which usually was set back on his head, was now drawn forward. He seemed to keep his face turned towards the big clap-board house, outside which stood a buggy with a pair of horses.

Despite the lilt of the song, the air of triumph in it, and the elation of the body engaged in a task suggestive of the pioneer-life—its roughness, its awkwardness, its undisciplined capacity, and its rugged, careless beauty, there was a curious watchfulness in the eyes, a smile of emotional expectancy at the lips—in a woman it would be called wistfulness. Indeed, there was something wistful in him too, strong man as he was. He was Irish, and the magic of imagination, with its accompanying sadness, lying behind all mirth and playfulness, was his. Yet he was an incorrigible optimist.

There was a time when he had been an incorrigible idler, a stoic—a thoroughly useless man. Those were the days when, having stepped into old Larry Brennan's house out of the rain, he had stayed ten years doing nothing, till a tragedy had roused him, brought him to his senses, set him upon the high-road of energy, action and success. Behind him, too, had been Norah Brennan and the Young Doctor—Norah, with such fine teeth in her head, though older than he when he married her, and the Young Doctor, with a pungent humour and good sense, which had stimulated and spurred him on.

Norah had not been his first love, but it seemed as though she would be his last one, for he had never looked right or left since he married her. The same old loyalty which had made him cling to the memory of the girl who threw him over long since at Enniskillen, in Old Ireland, still made him weave round Norah's head a halo of beauty—one of the blessings of imagination, for Norah was no Rose of Sharon.

Five years had gone since he had started the stage-coach from Askatoon to Cowrie, and began to breed and deal in horses; and the world had gone very well with him. He and the Young Doctor were partners in the horse-trading, and they had had as much fun as money out of the business.

He was thinking of the Young Doctor now, wondering why he did not come, protesting inwardly against the miserable delay, seething inwardly, though there was music on his tongue and a lilt to his voice. Round and round went the colt, growing more and more docile under the firm, quiet control of a born master of animals. Would the Young Doctor never come?

> "There was gatherin' of women, there was hush upon the stairway,
>   There was whisperin' and smilin', but it was no place for me;
> A little ship was comin' into harbour through the fairway—
>   It belongs to Mary Callaghan and me."

He had sung the verses over and over again—a dozen in all. It was like an obsession, and he was hardly aware of his own persistence—

> "He's the pride of Mary Callaghan and me!"

Five years since his own wedding with Norah, and no child—he had not realised when he married that it would be a miracle if a child came to them. In truth, he had not thought at all about that. They had gone through so much together in the days of tragedy, that being man and wife was the only thought in his mind when they went to the altar. But, with marriage, had come the other instinct, and he had dwelt much upon it. He wanted a child as the hart desires the water-springs; and Norah, knowing what was in his mind, willed it so with a will that was pathetic; for something, too, had been born in her which was not there before.

Marriage had made her see life with new eyes, and she had discovered many things hidden over forty years. Perhaps it was her great will and stubborn purpose which had at last wrung from the Great Creating Force assent to her diligent prayers, so that she was able to whisper something worth hearing into Nolan's ears one winter night, when the frost and ice outside were like a shrine for the warmth in their inflammable Irish souls.

Then the months of patient waiting had gone, with Nolan driving his four-horse—in the gaiety of his heart sometimes his six-horse—team, with his great red stage, and the coaching-horn defying the distant railway with shrill bravery, and receiving the shy congratulations of women-folk, and a hearty " Good-luck to ye ! " from men on every hand. He had become a figure in the West; and, having his millionaire brother-in-law, Terry Brennan, behind him, like a sounding-board, his fame, of its kind, was loud and reached far.

There had been many bets as to whether Norah would fulfil the natural hope of man, and when the time came the prairie people were wide-eyed with interest—for Norah was over forty.

The day had arrived. Would the Young Doctor never come out of that clap-board house which soaked the sun like a sponge, and yet was cooled within by the fresh breezes from the prairie? Was the Young Doctor bungling the business? was he——?

A man's figure appeared in the doorway, stood for an instant, with head bent and eyes upon the ground, as though to consider something; then there was a quick step to where Nolan stood with the sweating high-bred colt, which he had mastered.

As the Young Doctor came nearer, Nolan's eyes searched his face, then, with a puzzled look, he turned to the colt. " Steady, now, ye bunch o' beauty ! " he said. " We'll start ye soon. The trail's waitin' for ye."

" Nolan Doyle," said the Young Doctor, who understood the assumed indifference— that smooth, outer mask which holds the rough inner pain — " Nolan, you're wanted now."

" Did ye iver see a finer day ! " said Nolan, not able to look the Young Doctor in the eyes, for he knew that trouble of some dark

kind was come. "Norah 'll be glad it's a day like this—'Happy is the birth that the sun shines on,' happy are the dead that the rain rains on," he added; but his fingers trembled on the rein he held, as he quickly drew the colt nearer. "Ah, what *is* it, Doctor dear?" he suddenly burst out, with a note of agony in his voice. "Speak—what is it? Is all well? Is it over?"

The Young Doctor shook his head in negation and ruled his face to calmness.

"Then, what is it? Why are ye here? Doesn't she need you? Is it a thing to be done by any but you?"

"Be still, be still, Nolan," answered the other. "Keep a hand on yourself. You want a child—you want a child, I know"—he paused.

"God knows. What's to it all without a child? What should I be workin' for if it wasn't for a child? Well, then, the child, is it here?" he asked painfully.

"'Tis not here. She was no lass of twenty. 'Tis not here." The Young Doctor came nearer and laid a hand on Nolan's arm. "Steady now, and choose which it shall be—mother or child. It can't be both. I can save one or the other, not both. Which shall it be? She was no lass. Which shall it be? 'Tis for you to say."

The Young Doctor's words fell like the roar of a waterfall on his ears—"*Which shall it be—mother or child? It can't be both.*"

Was this, then, the end—Norah or Norah's child? How greatly he had longed for "the little imp," as he had sung but now! How had he thought always of a little lad, with hand in his, riding on the box beside him! How had the soul of him rung with the note of fatherhood!

"If it's she that's to stay, there could never be another child," said the Young Doctor.

"Never another, if it's she that's to stay," Nolan murmured, as though hardly grasping the tragic significance of the fact. Yet his face was white, and his eyes were dark with misery.

"You must say—now. There's no time. Is it to be the one you've not seen—or Norah?"

"What's that you're askin' me?" was the low, fierce reply. "God! don't you know? Go on, go on, and tell Norah that she's not to fret that it couldn't be. Go on—to Norah, man," he added, with a wild look in his eyes.

With swift steps the Young Doctor disappeared into the dark coolness of the house, leaving behind him the last hopes of a man whom he had helped in other days to set upon his feet and start again in life. "You couldn't be sure," he said to himself, as he entered the room where Norah struggled in that sea where man only stands upon the shore and watches till the storm goes down.

Heedless of the colt, which now ran about with the long rein trailing after it till a stable-boy, seeing, made it captive, Nolan sat upon the corner of a water-trough and looked at the house with eyes that saw only as through a dim grey atmosphere which stifled the brain and sense. Norah or the child! Did the Young Doctor believe him, then, the kind of man that . . .! But the thought of the little life that was his, his very own, which he had hoped to cheer him on, and make him work, and give him an end to aim at—it caught at his throat. And soon that little life would be lost, before the eyes had seen the sun, before the hands had reached out into the light of the world, before its voice had signalled back from sentient existence to the dim seas of being whence it had come, that it had found the shore.

In elementary understanding, he saw it all by virtue of the Celtic strain in him; and his brain swam on a flood of new impressions. He had leapt over vast spaces of life and experience in these few moments. How long he sat murmuring to himself, speaking Norah's name, bidding her not to mind—there were always the horses left!— he could not have told; but at last a woman came running from the house towards him. She was fat and scant of breath, and ere she reached him had no voice. Words failing her, she could only beckon to him.

"Is she safe?" he asked in a hoarse voice. Why should women be fat and scant of breath?

The woman nodded.

"Was it a boy?" he asked.

"Ah, a wonderful boy!" she said, "with a body like—like a young colt," she added, seeing the young-blooded horse led away.

"And the face of him?" he inquired anxiously.

The woman turned her head away. He understood. Life took its tribute through death, and, with a harsh hand, had destroyed its own.

"Norah is asking for you," the woman said. "There never was a braver. Ah, but there's a heart for you! No man deserves it. She would have gone and left the boy alive to you, if she'd known. She sez so. No man's worth it, that's my idee. But it wasn't to be, and it was flying in the face of Providence. But she did her best, poor dearie."

Nolan did not answer, but he could have throttled her for the truths she had uttered.

Inside the darkened room a few moments later, he turned away from the little lost life which a woman made ready for its return

to the nest of earth whence it had come. He bent over Norah's bed again.

"You're a fine woman, Norah," he said—"the very finest. Come, now, smile at me," he urged. "We've a long way to go together yet. Smile, Norah, girl. You're back again from the Bad Lands. Smile!"

With clouded eyes, Norah faintly smiled.

"You've a fine tooth in your head, Norah," he exclaimed—"as good as one that's twenty. I've broke the Inniskillen colt—a beauty," he added. "I'll bring him to your window to-morrow. You shall ride him next year. I'll give him to you. It's the best that's come from Queen of the Isles, tho' she's had twenty. There now, kape aisy."

"Can ye forgive me then, Nolan?" she asked brokenly. "Lord knows I ought to have wint instead. You'll want someone by you as the years go on—someone, somethin' to live for."

"Sure, you'll be by me, Norah."

"Come away," said the Young Doctor. "She must be left alone."

As Nolan left the room, he said again, "I'll bring the young colt to your window to-morrow."

Her eyes searched the room for what she had lost.

II

In vain. Norah had no comfort in the high-bred colt, no content in thinking that her own life had been spared. It seemed to her that, in spite of Nolan's cheery ways and whimsical talk and busy life, at the back of his eyes was a reproach; that in the tones of his voice was scorn of her, because she had failed to prove herself as good as any woman.

Norah never could realise, never had looked the fact in the face, that she was no longer a slip of a girl. Didn't her father and mother in the cottage under the Rise, whom she and Nolan, before they were married, had nursed back to life, and by which Nolan had paid the price of his ten years living on them—didn't they always treat her as a child almost? Had not the Young Doctor always addressed her as "Nolan's girl"? Hadn't he always said, "And how is Nolan's girl to-day, Mrs. Doyle?" Who had a better right to be so familiar with her! And Nolan himself, night and morning, wasn't it always, "Honey girl," and "Me child"?

How could she remember her age and the passing years? Her

waist was little bigger than at twenty, and her hair hung down to her knees. The wrinkles, did they not come from laughing at Nolan's jokes and her brother Shannon's whimsies? Did she not step as light as any lass that tripped to school? How could she remember her age? Yet in her heart of hearts there was no illusion.

There was a tiny grave just over the Rise, where an ash-tree stood like a sentinel in the gold-brown prairie. Its top could be seen from the window of the great living-room, and her eyes were ever looking that way, while Nolan's head was ever turned from it! Or, if his eyes fell on the tree, a look came into them as though a veil were drawn over his sight.

He talked faster and bustled more at such times, making a fuss at whatever he might be doing at the moment—lighting his pipe, sharpening the carving-knife, or mending a piece of harness. He never walked in that direction, if he could help it; but Norah stole away over the Rise to the whispering ash, every day in summer except a Sunday, when he was away with his stage-coach, or at a horse-fair, or buying or selling or training.

"Shure, 'tis not natural," said her father to her one bright, cold winter day, at the old man's cottage under the Rise; "'tis blasphemy to take on so, when it was the Lord's doin'. And it never lived at all—'twas held back from livin' by the hand o' God. Can't ye see? Are ye no Christian; are ye no philosopher, little girl?"

"I have no brains," she answered. "'Tis not what I was made for, studyin' out why this was done or wasn't. 'Tis enough to know 'twas done, an' what's come of its bein' done."

"And what's come of its bein' done, then— tell me that?" asked her mother, feebly lifting a cup of tea to her wrinkled mouth.

"Ah, what's come of it! Isn't he atin' his heart out—Nolan?"

"'Tis only your fancy. There never was a bolder tongue and a better man at table."

"Haven't I heard him singin'? 'Twas like a knife in me. Haven't I heard him talkin' in his sleep? 'Come on, then, me little lad. Up on the box wid ye!' and that kind of thing, he'd say. He's dreamin' now that never dreamt before out loud like that. 'Tisn't brains ye need to know truth. 'Tis a true heart and the quick ear of one that's got it."

" What was the song he sings that struck ye so ? " asked her father.
Her eyes took on a strange look as she recited Nolan's song:

> " Sure, the longest day has endin', and the wildest storm has fallin'—
> There's a young gossoon in yander, and he sits upon my knee ;
> There's a churchful for the christenin'—do you hear the imp a-callin' ?
> He's the pride of Mary Callaghan and me ! "

" It's like a man singin' to hide his shame," she added.

" What's that ye're sayin', Norah ? " asked her mother. " What's the shame y'are speakin' of, then ? "

With a sharp cry Norah stretched out her hands. The barriers that clouded her view of the exact truth had broken down. She saw the whole elementary facts in one revealing moment.

" Oh, shame it is to him that he's denied what is the pride of man," she said. " I know —ah, shure, I know ! I oughtn't to have married him. I made him do it—I made him. I drew him into it. 'Twas at the bedside of the two of ye that he ate the dish I made for him. I was never a wife for him—he that ought to have had a girl of twenty."

The true facts had possessed her at last. She saw herself, her vanity, her obtuseness, her self-deceit, her deception to him, laid bare.

" I'm older than him—I'm older," she went on. " I'm an old woman. I never was a wife for him, and he knows it, and he knew it from the first. And I couldn't carry it through with all my willin' and fightin'—'twas no matter for prayin' that, but just flyin' in the face of Providence. But the willin' and the fightin' come to nothin' ; and now he's off, he's off to one that's twenty. He's gone to one that's what I was long since, with hair like a sheaf of wheat in the sun, and the rest of her——"

Her hands dropped in despair, she sat down helplessly, and rocked backwards and forwards in her misery.

" Who's that you're speakin' of ? " said her father, with a furtive glance of understanding to her mother and a quick nod of comprehension. " Who's that with the harvest hair, and the rest of her——"

" A harvest for reapin' ! " Norah broke in, with a passionate gesture.

" Hush, for shame on ye ! " spoke her mother. " Have ye no

pride ? The man's yours, and he knows he's yours ; and what's to fear, I want to know ? "

Norah gave a bitter laugh. "D'ye think all men are like your own husband ? " she asked harshly. "Nolan's turned from me to *her*."

The old man got up and came over to her. "Who is she ? Where does she live ? Where does he see her, Norah girl ? " he asked.

She sprang to her feet. "Don't call me *girl* again ! " she cried. "I'm none o' that. I ought to have stayed with you. Shure, me spring was long since done. Me summer is that far gone, 'tis but a memory, and me winter's here. And it's cold—God knows it's cold ! " she said drearily.

"Who is she ? " urged her mother.

" 'Tis the sister of Jacques Charron, that keeps the tavern at Pardon's Drive. Nolan passes every day. He never misses a day with his stage-coach now—one day in going, and one day in coming, and the long night between."

"Peace, woman ! " said her father sharply. "Are ye mad ? "

"Last night, in his sleep, he said her name. And to-day he's gone to her. 'Tis not the stage day. He sent Shannon with the stage yesterday. But he couldn't stay away, so he's gone to her."

She turned towards the window, and watched the first flurries of a snowstorm coming over the prairie. "Ah, wurra, wurra ! I feel that I'd like the storm comin' there to swallow him up ; and me with him—and me with him! There'd be peace if the storm would swallow us up together."

"Poor lad! that would be hard on him," said the old man dryly, "if so be it's true that ye made him marry ye."

"'Twas his duty to stay true," said the old woman. "There was the marriage lines."

"Can ye rule the blood by lines on a paper?" said Norah, with a voice so cheerless that her father sat down by her and stroked her hand.

"I heard something about it," he said gently, "and I spoke to the Young Doctor about it; but he said, 'Lave be,' he said. ''Twill work itself out. The Charron girl yonder's a good girl, but only likin' to be noticed by a handsome man. Lave be, and he'll right himself,' he said. 'If he doesn't, ye can't cure it by interferin''—that's what he said; and he's a man that's got more sinse than you or me, or any of us."

Norah rose. "Yes, we'll lave be," she said. "What's the good of not lavin' it be? If I kill him I've lost him just as sure as if he wint with the girl. I've thought of killin' us both," she added, with a quiet glitter of her eyes, "but he'd leave me in Hell just the same if I did. But if the storm would do it—ay, if the storm would do it—together——"

The drifts of snow softly rising in the distance seemed to fascinate her eyes.

"You'd better be goin', Norah," said her mother solicitously. "You'll only get home now before the storm gets goin' hard."

Outside the door Norah turned and looked towards the barren arms of the ash-tree standing beside the grave of her baby that perished as it came. She made as if she would go to it through the snow, but changed her mind, and went down the slope to her house. Arrived there, she went straight to the barn and summoned one of the hands. A few minutes later, in the growing storm, with the wind becoming sharper every minute, she took the trail to Pardon's Drive alone.

A madness had seized her to go and bring Nolan back, or to go and take by the throat the girl that drew him away from her, or to die with him in the storm—in the soft, enfolding, quiet snow which had covered up so many tired pioneers of life.

She did not know quite why she went, but she felt that she must go. Some dark fascination of destiny was on her. The touch of the mystic in her Celtic blood stirred her, absorbed her. She was only conscious that she was driving, driving, and for ever driving towards Pardon's Drive. How long it was, how cold it was, how still it was, this long road to Pardon's Drive! Did Nolan find it so long as he drove day after day? Ah, no! Nolan found it short, for there was some one waiting at the end—a flower of life to be plucked for his wearing!

Words Nolan had sung in the days before their tragedy haunted her ears now, as the horses plunged through deeper and deeper snow, as the rugs on her knees became piled higher and higher with the soft flakes, as the drifts gathered heavier and heavier in the sleigh where she sat.

> "It was as fine a churchful as you ever clapt an eye on;
>   Oh, the bells was ringin' gaily, and the sun was shinin' free;
>   There was singers, there was clargy—'Bless you both,' says Father Tryon—
>   They was weddin' Mary Callaghan and me."

By and by it seemed that they made no progress. Heavily, with stupefying weariness, the horses ploughed their way through the snow. How many hours had she been going? She did not know. Night was falling, and she had no idea where she was, nor did she much care. The cold was numbing, and her body seemed to grow less and less material. She was like one that was slowly withdrawing her soul's self from its mortal home, leaving that home desolate and still and nerveless.

But the horses knew. They had been over this trail—how many hundred times! Their feet felt the true road under them—felt it, kept it. Their senses were concentrated on one thing—the end of the journey, rest, food, the warm stable at Pardon's Drive. Their tragedy would be in not getting there; Norah's tragedy might be—would it be?—in getting there.

None knows the silence of this world who has not been blanketed by falling snow and swept by drift. There is no universe, no time, nothing but this wheeling sphere of your own, in which you move alone—alone, the whole world dead but you.

Into this vast solitude, this silence, this dead world, a light suddenly pierced. It was the lantern hanging outside the door of Jacques Charron's tavern at Pardon's Drive.

Yet Norah did not move. She was like one who has lost consciousness of life and time.

They carried her in—it had not been easy to unloose her fingers from the reins. As she was laid down on a sofa she was only conscious of two things—the voice of a child, and the voice of Nolan. "Norah! Norah!" Nolan's voice called. It was so very far away.

At length she awoke, and it seemed to her that she had been asleep for years, so changed were her feelings, so peaceful was her mind. An old woman sat beside her, and leaned forward when her eyes opened.

"So. It is good. I tell them to leave you to me," the old woman said. "I have seen it, that cold. *Bien sûr!* I have seen them all stiff. It was not so with you. You had no heart to fight that cold—so, like that." The quizzical, kindly eyes searched Norah's. "*Bien,* it is good to sleep."

"How long have I slept ?—where am I ? " Norah asked.

" In Jacques Charron's house, so quiet and nice : *voilà* ! "

Again the old eyes searched Norah's face.

A cloud gathered in Norah's eyes. " Yes, I remember. 'Twas hard on the horses. 'Twas Nolan's best team. Are they all right ? Nolan 'd not like to see them bad."

Her eyes went round the room eagerly, plaintively, yet not with the bitter passion, the hopeless pain of—when was it ? How long was it since she came ? What had happened ? Where was Nolan ? The child's voice she heard—was it all a dream ?

Nolan's voice—had it been really Nolan's voice ? Had she imagined that his arms were round her, laying her down, stroking her face ?

" How long have I been here ? " she asked.

" *Quel heure ?* It was nine to the clock. Now it is twelve. *Certainement !* They have gone to bed, all but you and me, and——"

A child's voice rose plaintively in the night—so near. Why did it pierce to Norah's heart, make her tremble so ?

She raised herself on her elbow and turned in the direction of the small voice. The old woman opened a door softly, and made a gesture for her to see. Her heart stood still.

There, in a rocking-chair in the next room, in the red light of a great fire, sat the girl " with hair like a sheaf of wheat," and in her arms, pressed to her breast, was an infant, to whom she was crooning softly.

As Norah gazed with eyes that almost started from her head, a wild passion seized her. It was like some ether poured through her veins. Life seemed suddenly to expand in her. She was in a palpitating atmosphere which inflamed her whole being. She saw Nolan rise from a couch near the fire, come forward to the golden-haired girl, and touch the child's soft cheek with a forefinger.

" Little darlin'," he said, with a note in his voice that she had never heard in all the days they had lived together.

Then she went mad.

Nolan stepped back, startled, as she rushed forward into the room. In the red light of the fire, with her eyes blazing, her arms outstretched, her fingers crooked like some bird of prey, she looked like an avenger in a Greek tragedy.

" 'Tis as I thought!" she said in a whisper, her lips so dry with passion that she could scarcely speak. " 'Tis as I said! 'Twas for this I was left alone yonder, while the wanton had her way!"

With a startled cry the Charron girl got to her feet with the child, and at first she trembled so that the babe almost fell from her arms; but presently a dark flush of indignation passed over her face, and she drew herself up with pride. If anger could have killed, Norah must have died there before her.

"*Imbecile*—fool!" she said, and when she opened her mouth a finer set of teeth showed than Norah had in her head, and that was saying much.

"Hush, hush—the baby!" said Nolan, and stepped forward towards it. Norah made as though she would come between, but Nolan's arm shot out before her.

"Wait! You will wake the child," he said quietly. He took it tenderly from the girl's arms and placed it in those of the old woman, who, entering with Norah, had stood with ironical humour watching the drama. She was so old that her pulses were not disturbed by the passions of others; but such scenes as these gave sensations which replaced the stirring episodes of youth and middle age. She took the child gently and put its fresh cheek to hers, quavering an old French chanson:

> " J'ai faim, j'ai froid !
> Pitié ! noble dame ;
> J'ai faim, j'ai bien froid,
> Prenez pitié de moi—
> Prenez pitié de moi."

"Into the other room, Ma'am Charron!" said Nolan. "For a minute then—'tis not for a child's ears this."

He was very quiet, and his eyes dwelt on Norah's face with a look of command when he turned round again to the women standing in the light of the fire. Then he said to the girl:

" Sure, you had better go, Annette. There are things to say."

" Yes, there are things to say," interjected Norah, trembling. " And you had better stay—*Annette !* "

There was a scorn and an anger in the last word which made Annette's blood tingle.

" What have you to say to me ? " she asked Norah fiercely. Her eyes seemed as red as the fire that burned on the hearth.

" Is there no shame in ye ? " said Norah. " I'm his wife. Did ye need to stay and shame me with——"

" Madame, you are a liar, and you are a fool. If I was a man I would kill you." Annette Charron's fingers twitched.

"Ye flaunt the child in my face——" Norah burst out in a high-pitched voice, but got no further, for Nolan caught her arm with a grip that made her cry out.

"Be still, woman!" he said in a voice gone suddenly hard. "Would ye wake the dead? Can't ye let the dead lie in peace with the promise I made—with the promise I made!"

"What dead?" asked Norah in a trembling voice, for it came upon her all at once that she had blundered.

"Can't ye be kind"—Nolan protested—"you that's just back from the dead, Norah? A little longer out in the snow and you'd have been lyin' as she is lyin' in there." He jerked his head towards another room with a closed door.

"Who is lyin' in there?" Norah asked with trembling lips.

"The mother of that," he added, with a nod towards the child, which Madame Charron was crooning to sleep. "She was caught in the storm too, but it was too strong for her. She gave the child all the warmth she had. And a fine boy it is, the finest iver was almost."

With a cry that came as though from a spirit released from prison, Norah swayed, then, fainting, she fell forward. Annette Charron caught her as she fell. She and Nolan laid her on the sofa, and together they set about restoring her, while the old woman watched from the doorway, irony still in her look.

"A good match it would have been," the old woman said to herself. "A fine man to see—that Nolan! If I had been Annette, I would have scratch' her eyes out," she added. "But Annette's a good girl of her kind," she murmured as an afterthought.

"You'll forgive her?" said Nolan gently to the girl. "'Twas a madness in her, shure."

The girl looked at him for a moment very steadily, and seemed about to speak, but instead, she turned away for a moment and busied herself with adjusting Norah's head to the pillow.

"Then, don't you be hard on her—ever," she said presently, with meaning in her tone and a face grown pale again after the passion of the last few moments.

"Oh, I've never been hard on her, and never will," answered Nolan.

"M'sieu' Nolan, you are a fool," rejoined the girl sharply. . . . "There, she is coming-to—make her understand the truth," she said firmly. "Make her understand—*absolument*. I am going to bed," she added, and before he could say more, she was gone.

In her place came the old woman with the child. "It was time Annette went to bed," she said dryly.

Presently Norah's eyes opened, and rested on Nolan's face. Her hand was in his. There was that look in his eyes she had never seen before.

"Who was she?" asked Norah.

"Annette? You know—as good a girl as any, as——"

"No, the dead woman in there," she pointed feebly to the other room.

"'Twas a stranger, come from buryin' her man in the north. And now she's gone, poor woman."

Suddenly he leaned over Norah. "What made ye come here, Norah? What were ye after?"

"Where should a woman be but with her husband?" she answered evasively.

"Thrue for ye," he said, with a strange look. He knew that he had torn her heart. "Thrue for ye. Where should she be except with her husband—and the child?"

She stared at him. Her face grew white. "The child!" she repeated anxiously. "Shure, I have no head, Nolan. I don't see at all, at all. I am sorry I spoke so wild and bad to the girl, but there was something in me that drove me crazy. I don't understand, Nolan dear."

"I've made the child me own, Norah—me own for iver and iver. I promised the dead woman I'd do it. I promised for you and for me. She was a fine woman, about your age"—ah, the incomparable liar!—"and she wint away at peace; for she saw in me the makin' of a fine father to her child. Are ye with me in this, Norah?"

Norah saw a light glimmer out of the dark, which would grow and grow to a wide radiance, would lighten all her world.

"Oh, give me the child!" she cried, all the mother-hunger in her, her face glowing, her hands outstretched. The old woman put the babe in her arms. She pressed it to her breast passionately.

Nolan watched her with a wonderful look of pride and content in his face.

"We'll make-believe," he said gaily to her in a whisper.

"There's no make-believe," she answered, with a look of fierceness almost. "It come to me out of the storm—'tis mine, 'tis mine!"

"*Acushla*," said Nolan gaily, "'tis yours then;" and he touched the child's cheek.

The next morning, when they left, Nolan's good-bye and his gay wink and word to Annette, with the hair like a harvest of wheat in the sun, were careless enough for Norah to be sure that the farewell of its kind was final. And so it was. But Annette—who knows? The heart of a woman is a strange thing.

THE
MAN OF WORDS
By Mrs. Henry de la Pasture
(LADY CLIFFORD)

Paintings and Drawings by
W. Heath Robinson

THE old lord to the goose-girl said,
"'Tis not your beauty that I prize,
Nor raven hair that crowns your head,
Nor slender waist, nor soft grey eyes.

"I love you for your simple truth
And for the mind and soul of you.
And would the gods but grant me youth,
I straight would be your husband true.

"But I am withered, worn and grim,
And you a flower fresh and wild,
And all the world makes mock of him
Who, in his dotage, weds a child."

The old lord to the goose-girl said,
With courteous smile and silver tongue,
"I love you and I fain would wed—
But I'm too old, and you're too young.

" And yet withal I do admit,
    So gentle and so grave your mien,
So low your voice, so kind your wit,
    One would suppose you bred a queen.

" No high-born dame could please me more,
    And would the gods but grant to me
To lose of all my years a score,
    Then we might wed right faithfully.

" So we would make Old Time confess
    (Who brings mankind to sure decay)
We loved each other none the less
    For eyes grown dim and heads grown grey."

With blush of peach and candid eyes
    The goose-girl answered straight and free,
" To be your wife I fain would rise,
    For I love you as you love me."

The goose-girl said, with heart on fire,
    " Oh, what is age when love is true ?
No dearer mate could I desire,
    I love the noble words of you.

" And since 'tis not my looks you prize,
    And since 'tis youth for which you pine—
I've nothing else to sacrifice—
    I'll pray the gods to grant you mine."

A passing cupid caught the sigh,
    And bore it in a crystal dish
On his swift flight from earth to sky.
    Jove, smiling, said, " *I grant that wish.*"

The old lord dropped of years a score,
    Each shrunken limb grew round and fair,
In manhood's prime he stood once more,
    Back to his temples stole his hair.

The old lord's sunken jaw plumped out,
    His teeth stood firm, his eyes shone clear.
He was as straight and strong and stout
    As man could be at forty year.

The goose-girl took his load of years
  That on her shoulders now was cast.
She knew no doubts, she knew no fears,
  She kissed Love's hand that bound it fast.

Her fleeting charms of youth were lost;
  A buxom dame with comely face
And raven hair just touched with frost
  Stood smiling in the goose-girl's place.

Full wistfully she looked at him,
  Nor needed words his blank dismay.
Her candid eyes grew something dim,
  Love shut his wings and stole away.

She stood alone—unseen, unheard—
  And pondered, wondering, o'er the change.
"I did but take him at his word.
  And oh," she said, "but men are strange!"

Then homeward trudging—on her staff
  She leaned a trifle heavily—
Her wise eyes wrinkled with a laugh.
  "*He was a man o' words!*" quoth she.

OLD · BRAND

By Neil Munro

Drawings by G. Barrow

WHEN I was on the *Courier* first (and which particular *Courier* it was may as well remain unmentioned), it had an editor whose pride was in the fact that no other provincial paper in the country gave such prompt, copious, and well-informed obituaries as his. The breath was hardly out of a J.P., or even a local police-constable, when a neat and comprehensive biography was being set up in the case-room. Nothing was overlooked—the unfailing geniality of the deceased, his kindness to the poor, his renown as a pansy-grower, or his relationship to a Procurator-Fiscal. Invariably his demise " cast a gloom over the whole community." The promptness and the profoundly sympathetic spirit of our obituaries divested death of no small part of its terror. We depended for our circulation less upon football than upon the bereaved. An obituary of ours was always couched in language which made the surviving members of the family our friends and subscribers for life. The study of the obituaries in our files for twenty years would suggest that nobody ever died in the district except people of the most angelic character.

Old Brand, the editor, of course, got all the popular credit for this, and many a bag of potatoes. When any of the neighbouring farmers fell into the decline of years, or was in extremity as a result of some accident with a gig driving home at night at the end of too prolonged a sitting in the Blue Bell Inn on a market day, the family would take anticipatory steps to secure his posthumous reputation by sending a couple of ducks or a middle of pork to the editor of the *Courier*. You never saw a fatter man ; for twenty years he battened on bereavement. On the wall above his desk he had pasted a list of words and phrases appropriate to these sad occasions—"release," "gone to his rest," "pay the debt to nature," "the way of all flesh," "joined the great majority," "long home," "gathered to his fathers," "retained all his faculties to the last," "we shall never look upon his like again," "sorrowing relatives," "the Reaper has been busy this week," and so on. It was the days before half-tone picture-blocks were in the news-papers, but Old Brand anticipated all the artistic pleasure of the editor of to-day, on those weeks when a more than usually important demise justified turned rules for mourning borders.

"Poor Bailie Webster!" he would say. "He's gone at last; but I think we have a very satisfactory notice of him. Fancy the *Telegraph* with only a quarter-a-column!" And he would generously drench himself with snuff—his way of handing himself a bouquet in acknow-ledgment of his efficiency as editor.

But the fact was that Old Brand got the glory and the ducks that by rights belonged to me and my predecessors as reporters of the *Courier*. Any expedition or any literary art that might be manifest in the production of obituaries were due to us. It was I who added "Charon's ferry," and "crossed to the Stygian shore," to Old Brand's mortuary thesaurus; I can prove it by the files. Brand, to be quite frank about it, had no sense of Style; a good enough man in many ways, and able, with the aid of the *Scotsman, Herald*, and *Daily News*, to turn out a quite plausible leading article, but with not a gleam of inspiration when thrown upon his own resources. When I introduced "the blind Fury with the abhorred shears" (a rather neat thing of Milton's) into an obituary notice of a local tailor, Old Brand cut it out of my copy as being rather personal. Any touch like that, with what I con-sidered literary grace and the charm of novelty, he would smother remorselessly. "Just stick to the facks, James," he would say; "and don't be flimboyant. Facks! That's the mainstay of the *Courier*. Facks, and a kindly tolerant spirit when it comes to obituaries."

In a press behind a discarded Eagle bill-machine we had what we called our Mortuary. There, alphabetically ar-ranged pigeon-holes accommodated some fifteen or sixteen hundred obituaries of eminent local men who had yet to qualify for editorial treatment. Every man with a villa, a farm, a shop that advertised, or a reputation for fancy dogs and poultry, had his career and his achievements duly chronicled. When nothing else was doing, Brand expected me to bring these memoirs up to date, a task succinctly marked down in the reporter's book as "Stiffs." The solemn archives had been growing for many years; some of the pigeon-holes were tightly crammed; it was a heartbreak to Old Brand that the "M's" appeared to be immortal.

" Aren't the deevils dour ! " he would explain, peering into the Mortuary through his great gold-rimmed spectacles.

To prepare a man's obituary for a newspaper has often been observed to postpone indefinitely a dissolution that appeared imminent. The favourite practical joke of Providence is to catch the newspapers unprepared, and very often, when the doctors had given up a patient whose record in our Mortuary was somewhat out of date, I had only to skirmish around for fresh details and add some lines about his having won the black-faced wedder medal in 1886, and the patient was sure of a miraculous recovery. This was, I am certain, the reason why Old Brand always instructed me to make my inquiries with caution and delicacy. I fancy he had an idea that Providence could be outwitted.

When Willie Young, of the Driepps, the famous Clydesdale breeder, was *in extremis*, and I hurriedly gathered the later facts which were to make his obituary in the *Courier* consolatory to his family, he, of course, recovered immediately, to the professional chagrin of Brand, who used to play whist with him every Saturday.

" You must have gone about splairgin' at large for your facks, James," said my editor. " Amn't I aye tellin' you to be judicious ? Mr. Young was as good as deid when I spoke to you in the mornin'."

He could not take a walk along the street at any time without encountering healthy-looking men whom secretly he regarded as enemies of the *Courier* ; they had turned the corner and jinked Atropos after the editor had been at the pains to add with his own hand the final eulogistic phrases to their memoirs as prepared by his reporters.

On one occasion Providence caught us badly unprepared with the facts to do justice to the memory of a prominent townsman who had only recently come to the place, and the *Telegraph* beat us by about a column. The circumstances were all the more vexatious since the deceased was a man well stricken in years, whose failing condition had been commented on for weeks.

" Oh, James ! " wailed Mr. Brand. " You saw the man at the Cattle Show on Wednesday ; you might have had the common sense to see he would soon be needin' our attention ! Tchk ! Tchk ! Tchk ! Isn't it deplorable ! There you were on Saturday, wastin' your time wi' the notice of Ninian Taylor, and him away, as cocky as you like, to Callander Hydropathic on the Monday ! "

This bad break revolutionised Old Brand's ideas of how I was to attend to the Mortuary. Henceforth, instead of sitting in the office systematically going through the alphabet and patching up the memoirs of folk who seemed to have an unconscionable repugnance to dying, I was to daunder along the street and keep a shrewd look-out for elderly citizens showing signs of breaking up. If their identity was unknown to me I was to follow them up, discover where they stayed, and thereafter push judicious inquiries. More than once, on the track of some tottering old gentleman at dusk, who little suspected the honour I proposed to do him, I was suspected of designs upon his purse.

It was an extraordinary town for tottering old gentlemen, though I had never observed the fact before. The shortcomings of our Mortuary were lamentably disclosed; my predecessors had failed to secure the memoirs of hundreds of men who, in the ordinary course of nature, might require the alleviatory attentions of the *Courier* at any moment. The "M's" in the Mortuary overflowed into the "Q" recess. I acquired the furtive, speculative eye of an undertaker.

Nevertheless, Old Brand had rarely a worse year so far as concerned the Mortuary. It seemed as if I had only to cast my speculative eye upon any wreck of a man to endow him with something like the sprightliness and health of youth. "You're the most unlucky reporter we ever had, James," said Old Brand. "There you are, slavin' away at the Mortuary, and I haven't had the chance to put the finish on a body for nearly a month!"

So desperate did he become about the situation that he led me once into an awkward fix. He came in one morning to the office with a brisk, exhilarated manner, and the news that Watty Rigg, the Cattle Auctioneer, was gone. "Slipped away at eight o'clock this morning, I hear," said the editor; "and, with no ill-will to Watty, I regard it as most considerate—most considerate! It's seldom they do me the justice to wait for the day we go to press. It's eighteen years since your predecessor, Cameron, had him snodded off in the Mortuary. Watty was not exactly a Prince in Israel, but I never saw a bonnier curler, and we'll have to do the best we can to gratify his widow. You'll slip over to The Holm and get a few particulars about his Christian resignation. Now be sure and go about the thing with delicacy and caution."

I would appear not to have gone about the thing with sufficient delicacy and caution to outwit Providence, for when I went to The Holm, and intimated to Mrs. Rigg the object of my mission, I discovered that her husband was alive! What was worse, hearing who the visitor was, and surmising the occasion of his call, Watty Rigg insisted that I should be taken in to see him!

"Ye're the lad frae the *Courier*," he said, propped up in bed, with

weeping folk about him. "I aye tak' oot your paper, though it's no' worth a d——n for fat-stock prices. Ye'll be wantin' a few tit-bits. Tell Mr. Brand I'm no' for nane o' his maudlin' sentiment. I was jist Watty Rigg the cattleman. Put that doon! I—I never gied naebody naething unless I got the value o't, and there's nae use tellin' ony lies aboot it. I was just an ordinar' business man, and I had a family to provide for. I never was a pattern to onybody, and I didna try. Mind this—I never had ony fancy relatives wi' a grand poseetion; I left the schule when I was ten, and I never could write my name, but I built a business!—a business! Put that doon! There was nane o' the gentle Jeremiah aboot the late Walter Rigg; he was a gey hard nut, and he found a lot o' hard yins biddin' against him. He wasna a model father, nor ony great catch as a husband, and don't you, for your life, say that he was! But at the worst he never was a hypocrite. And this is a thing ye'll have to tak' a note o'—he didna die in Christian resignation like a' the other peelywally folk that figure in the *Courier*; he died as dour as a brock, but he didna go to his Judge wi' false pretences!"

When I returned to Old Brand with this remarkable story, he almost wept. "Still lingerin' on!" said he, despairingly. "Isn't he the frightened coward! I doubt, James, you have been splairgin' noisily, as usual, in your inquiries."

I am glad to say Watty Rigg, apparently relieved by his confidence to me, made a wonderful recovery, and, as far as I know, lives till this day.

But Old Brand himself is now, as he would have put it, "beyond these voices." My speculative eye discerned one day that he, too, was a tottering old gentleman, and, to put Providence off the trail of one I loved despite his literary disabilities, I carefully prepared his obituary in my lodgings. It was affection, not my taste, that made me load the notice with the hackneyed phrases he had used, himself, so often.

For weeks I kept it in my desk. "How goes the Mortuary, James?" he one day asked me wearily. "I hope you're keepin' it up; we must always send them off like gentlemen," and he read no menace in my furtive eye.

But Providence, for once, was not stalled off at the sight of a complete obituary in readiness; a few days later we had to turn the leads for Old Brand's memoir in the *Courier*.

THE DANE'S BREECHIN'

By E. Œ. Somerville and "Martin Ross"

Drawings by Leo Cheney

THE story begins at the moment when my brother Robert and I had made our final arrangements for the fishing expedition. We had ordered a car from Coolahan's public-house in the village; an early lunch was imminent.

The latter depended upon Julia; in fact it would be difficult to mention anything at Wavecrest Cottage that did not depend on Julia. We, who were but strangers and sojourners (the cottage with the beautiful name having been lent to us, with Julia, by an aunt), felt that our very existence hung upon her clemency. How much more, then, luncheon, at the revolutionary hour of a quarter to one? Even courageous people are afraid of other people's servants, and Robert and I were far from being courageous. Possibly this is why Julia treated us with compassion, even with kindness—especially Robert.

"Ah, poor Masther Robert!" I have heard her say to a friend in the kitchen, who was fortunately hard of hearing, " ye wouldn't feel him in the house no more than a feather! An' indeed, as for the two o' thim, sich gallopers never ye seen! It's hardly they'd come in the house to throw the wet boots off thim! Thim'd gallop the woods all night like the deer!"

At half-past twelve, all being in train, I went to the window to observe the weather, and saw a covered car with a black horse plodding along the road that separated the cottage that had been lent us by my aunt from the seashore.

A covered car is a vehicle peculiar to the south of Ireland. Its mouth is at the back, and it has the sinister quality of totally concealing its occupants until the irrevocable moment when it is turned and backed against your front door steps. For this moment my brother Robert and I did not wait. A short passage and a flight of steps separated us from the kitchen; beyond the steps, and facing the kitchen door, a door opened into the garden. Robert slipped up heavily in the passage as we fled, but gained the garden door undamaged. The hall-door bell pealed at my ear; I caught a glimpse of Julia, the "general," pounding chops with the rolling-pin.

137

"Say we're out," I hissed to her—"gone out for the day! We are going into the garden!"

"Sure ye needn't give yerself that much trouble," replied Julia affably, as she snatched a grimy cap off a nail.

Nevertheless, in spite of the elasticity of Julia's conscience, the garden seemed safer.

There was not a moment to lose. We plunged into the raspberry bushes, and, crouched beneath their embowered arches, the fullness of the situation began to sink into our souls.

With Aunt Dora's house we had taken on, as it were, her practice, and the goodwill of her acquaintance. The Dean of Glengad and Mrs. Doherty were the very apex and flower of the latter, and in the party now installed in Aunt Dora's drawing-room I unhesitatingly recognised them, and Mrs. Doherty's sister, Miss McEvoy. Miss McEvoy was an elderly lady of the class usually described as being "not all there." The expression, I imagine, implies a regret that there should not be more. As, however, what there was of Miss McEvoy was chiefly remarkable for a monstrous appetite and a marked penchant for young men, it seems to me mainly to be regretted that there should be as much of her as there is.

After a brief interval of considerable mental strain, the door into the garden opened and Julia came forth, with a spotless apron and a face of elaborate unconcern. She picked a handful of parsley, her black eyes questing for us among the bushes; they met mine, and a glance more alive with conspiracy it has not been my lot to receive. She moved desultorily towards us, gathering green gooseberries in her apron.

"I told them the two o' ye were out," she murmured to the gooseberry bushes. "They axed when would ye be back. I said ye went to town on the early thrain and wouldn't be back till night.

Decidedly Julia's conscience could stand alone.

"With that then," she continued, "Miss McEvoy lands into the hall, an' ' O Letitia,' says she, ' those must be the gentleman's fishing rods!' and then 'Julia!' says she, 'could ye give us a bit o' lunch?' That one's the imp!"

"Look here!" said Robert hoarsely, and with the swiftness of panic, "I'm off! I'll get out over the back wall. There's Coolahan's Pub.: we'll get something to eat there."

What Mrs. Coolahan thought, as we dived, hatless, from the sunlight into her dark shop, did not appear; what she looked was consternation.

"Luncheon!" she repeated with stupefaction—"luncheon! The dear help us, I have no luncheon for the like o' ye!"

"Oh, anything will do," said Robert cheerfully. His experiences at the London bar had not instructed him in the commissariat of his country. "A bit of cold beef, or just some bread and cheese."

Mrs. Coolahan's bleared eyes rolled wildly to mine, as seeking sympathy and sanity.

"With the will o' Pether!" she exclaimed, "how would I have cold beef? And as for cheese——!" She paused, and then, curiosity overpowering all other emotions, "What ails Julia Cronelly at all, that your honour's ladyship is comin' to the like o' this dirty place for your dinner?"

"Oh, Julia's run away with a soldier!" struck in Robert brilliantly.

"Small blame to her if she did itself!" said Mrs. Coolahan, gallantly accepting the jest without a change of her enormous countenance; "she's a long time waiting for the chance! Maybe ourselves 'd go if we were axed! I have a nice bit of salt pork in the house," she continued: "would I give your honours a rasher of it?"

We adventured ourselves into the unknown recesses of the house, and sat gingerly on greasy horsehair-seated chairs, in the parlour, while the bubbling cry of the rasher and eggs arose to heaven from the frying-pan, and the reek filled the house as with a grey fog. Potent as it was, it but faintly foreshadowed the flavour of the massive slices that presently swam in briny oil on our plates. But we had breakfasted at eight; we tackled them with determination, and without too nice inspection of the three-pronged forks. We drank porter, we achieved a certain sense of satiety, that on very slight provocation would have broadened into nausea or worse. All the while the question remained in the balance as to what we were to do for our hats, and for the myriad baggage involved in the expedition.

We finally decided to write a minute inventory of what was indispensable, and to send it to Julia by the faithful hand of Croppy, Mrs. Coolahan's car-driver.

By the malignity that governed all things on that troublous day, neither of us had a pencil, and Mrs. Coolahan

had to be appealed to. That she had by this time properly grasped the position was apparent in the hoarse whisper in which she said, carefully closing the door after her :

" The Dane's coachman is inside ! "

Simultaneously Robert and I removed ourselves from the purview of the door.

" Don't be afraid," said our hostess reassuringly, " he'll never see ye—sure I have him safe back in the snug ! Is it a writing-pin ye want, Miss ? " she continued, moving to the door. " Katty Ann ! Bring me in the pin out o' the office ! "

The Post Office was, it may be mentioned, a department of the Coolahan public-house, and was managed by a committee of the younger members of the Coolahan family. These things are all, I believe, illegal, but they happen in Ireland. The committee was at present, apparently, in full session, judging by the flood of conversation that flowed in to us through the open door. The request for the pen caused an instant hush, followed after an interval by the slamming of drawers and other sounds of search.

" Ah, what's on ye delaying this way ? " said Mrs. Coolahan irritably, advancing into the shop. " Sure I seen the pin with Helayna this morning."

At the moment all that we could see of the junior postmistress was her long bare shins, framed by the low-browed doorway, as she stood on the counter to further her researches on a top shelf.

" The Lord look down in pity on me this day ! " said Mrs. Coolahan, in exalted and bitter indignation, " or on any poor creature that's striving to earn her living and has the likes o' ye to be thrusting to ! "

We here attached ourselves to the outskirts of the search, which had by this time drawn into its vortex a couple of countrywomen with shawls over their heads, who had hitherto sat in decorous but observant stillness in the background. Katty Ann was rapidly examining tall bottles of sugar-stick, accustomed receptacles apparently for the pen, Helayna's raven fringe showed traces of a dive into the flour-bin. Mrs. Coolahan remained motionless in the midst, her eyes fixed on the ceiling, an exposition of suffering and of eternal remoteness from the ungodly.

We were now aware for the first time of the presence of Mr. Coolahan, a taciturn person, with a blue-black chin and a gloomy demeanour.

" Where had ye it last ? " he demanded.

" I seen Katty Ann with it in the cow-house, sir," volunteered a small female Coolahan from beneath the flap of the counter.

Katty Ann, with a vindictive eye at the tell-tale, vanished.

At this juncture I mounted on an up-ended barrel to investigate a

promising lair above my head, and from this altitude was unexpectedly presented with a bird's-eye view of a hat with a silver band inside the railed and curtained "snug." I descended swiftly, not without an impression of black bottles on the snug table; and Katty Ann here slid in from the search in the cow-house.

"'Twasn't in it," she whined, "nor I didn't put it in it."

"Look here!" said Robert abruptly, "this business is going on for a week. I'm going for the rods myself."

There comes, with the most biddable of men, a moment when argument fails, the moment of dead pull, when the creature perceives his own strength, and the astute will give in, early and imperceptibly, in order that he may not learn it beyond forgetting.

The only thing left to be done now was to accompany Robert, to avert what might be irretrievable disaster.

Again we scaled the garden-wall, and glided as before through the raspberry bushes. At the kitchen door we were instantly met by Julia, with her mouth full, and a cup of tea in her hand. She drew us into the kitchen.

"Where are they, Julia?" I whispered. "Have they had lunch?"

"Is it lunch?" replied Julia, through bread and butter; "there isn't a bit in the house but they have it ate! And the eggs I had for the fast-day for myself, didn't That One"—I knew this to indicate Miss McEvoy—"ax an omelette from me when she seen she had no more to get!"

"Are they out of the dining-room?" broke in Robert.

"Faith, they are. 'Twas no good for them to stay in it! That One's lying up on the sofa in the dhrawing-room like any owld dog, and the Dane and Mrs. Doherty's dhrinking hot water—they have bad shtomachs, the craytures."

Robert opened the kitchen door and crept towards the dining-room, wherein, not long before the alarm, had been gathered all the essentials of the expedition. I followed him. I have never committed a burglary, but since the moment when I creaked past the drawing-room door, foretasting the instant when it would open, my sympathies are dedicated to burglars.

In two palpitating journeys we removed from the dining-room our belongings, and placed them in the kitchen; silence, fraught with dire possibilities, still brooded over the drawing-room. Could they all be asleep, or was Miss McEvoy watching us through the keyhole? There remained only my hat, which was upstairs; and at this, the last moment, Robert remembered his fly-book, left under the clock in the dining-room. I again passed the drawing-room in safety, and got upstairs, Robert effecting at the same moment his third entry into the dining-room. I was in the act of thrusting in the second hat-pin when I heard the drawing-room door open. I admit that, obeying the primary instinct of self-preservation, my first impulse was to lock myself in; it passed, aided by the recollection that there was no key. I made for the landing, and from thence viewed, in a species of trance, Miss McEvoy crossing the hall and entering the dining-room. A long and deathly pause followed. She was a small woman; had Robert strangled her? After two or three horrible minutes a sound reached me—the well-known rattle of the sideboard drawer. All, then, was well—Miss McEvoy was probably looking for the biscuits, and Robert must have escaped in time through the window. I took my courage in both hands and glided downstairs. As I placed my foot on the oilcloth of the hall, I was confronted by the nightmare spectacle of my brother creeping towards me on all-fours through the open door of the dining-room, and then, crowning this already over-loaded moment, there arose a series of blood-curdling yells from Miss McEvoy.

It seems to me that the next incident was the composite and shattering collision of Robert, Julia and myself in the scullery doorway, followed by the swift closing of the scullery door upon us by Julia; then the voice of the Dean of Glengad, demanding from the house at large an explanation, in a voice of cathedral severity.

"Julia! Where is the man who was secreted under the dinner-table?"

I gripped Robert's arm. The issues of life and death were now in Julia's hands.

"Is it who was in the dining-room, your Reverence?" asked Julia, in tones of respectful honey; "sure that was the carpenter's boy, that came to quinch a rat-hole. Sure we're destroyed with rats."

"But," pursued the Dean, raising his voice to overcome Miss McEvoy's continuous screams of explanation to Mrs. Doherty, "I understand that he left the room on his hands and knees. He must have been drunk!"

"Ah, not at all, your Reverence," replied Julia, with almost compassionate superiority; "sure that poor boy is the gentlest crayture ever came into a house. I suppose 'tis what it was he was ashamed like when Miss McEvoy comminced to screech, and faith he never stopped nor stayed till he ran out of the house like a wild goose!"

We heard the Dean reascend the kitchen steps, and make a statement of which the words "drink" and "Dora" alone reached us. The drawing-room door closed, and in the release from tension I sank heavily down upon a heap of potatoes. The wolf of laughter that had been gnawing at my vitals broke loose.

" Why did you go out of the room on your hands and knees ? " I moaned, rolling in anguish on the potatoes.

" I got under the table when I heard the brute coming," said Robert, with the crossness of reaction from terror; " then she settled down to eat biscuits, and I thought I could crawl out without her seeing me——"

" *Ye can come out !* " said Julia's mouth, appearing at a crack of the scullery door. " I have as many lies told for ye—God forgive me !—as'd bog a noddy ! " This mysterious contingency might have impressed us more had the artist been able to conceal her legitimate pride in her handiwork. We emerged from the chill and varied smells of the scullery, retaining just sufficient social self-control to keep us from flinging ourselves with grateful tears upon Julia's neck. Shaken as we were, the expedition still lay open before us ; the game was in our hands. We were winning by tricks, and Julia held all the honours.

II

Perhaps it was the clinging memory of the fried pork; perhaps it was the result of reaction after shock, but there was no doubt that the expedition languished.

There was no fault to be found with the setting. The pool in which the river coiled itself under the pine-trees was black and brimming, the fish were rising at the flies that wrought above it, like a spotted-net veil in hysterics, the distant hills lay in sleepy undulations of every shade of blue, the grass was warm, and not unduly peopled with ants. But some impalpable blight was upon us. We cast our choicest flies, with delicate quiverings, with coquettish withdrawals ; had they been cannon-balls they could hardly have had a more intimidating effect upon the trout. Where we fished a Sabbath stillness reigned, beyond that charmed area they rose like notes of exclamation in a French novel. I was on the whole inclined to trace these things back to the influence of the pork, working on systems weakened by panic ; but Robert was not in the mood to trace them to anything. Unsuccessful fishermen are not fond of introspective suggestions. The member of the expedition who enjoyed himself beyond any question was Mrs. Coolahan's car-horse. Having been taken out of the shafts on the road above the river, he had, with his harness on his back, like Horatius, fallen to luxurious grazing along the river's edge, while his driver smoked, no less luxuriously, in the background.

It was there that I first came to notice a fact whose bearing upon our fortunes I was far from suspecting. The old horse's harness was of dingy brown leather, while, in remarkable contrast to the rest of the outfit, the breeching was of solid and well-polished black leather, with silver buckles. It was not so much the discrepancy of the breeching as its respectability that jarred upon me; finally I commented upon it to Croppy.

His cap was tilted over his nose; he glanced at me sideways from under its peak.

"Sure the other breechin' was broke, and if that owld shkin was to go the lin'th of himself without a breechin' on him he'd break all before him! There was some fellas took him to a funeral one time without a breechin' on him, an' when he seen the hearse what did he do but to rise up in the sky!"

Wherein lay the moral support of a breeching in such a contingency it is hard to say. I accepted the fact without comment, and expressed a regret that we had not been indulged with the entire set of black harness.

Croppy measured me with his eye, grinned bashfully, and said:

"Sure it's the Dane's breechin' we have, Miss! I daresay he'd hardly get home at all if we took any more from him!"

"The Dane" was the Dean of Glengad.

"Croppy," I said, a sudden alarm chilling me to the marrow, "how did you get it? Can they get home without it?"

"Arrah, why not, Miss? That black horse of the Dane's wouldn't care if there was nothing at all on him!"

It was past five o'clock, and a threatening range of clouds was rising from seaward across the west. Things had been against us from the first, and if the last stone in the sling of Fate was that we were to be wet through before we got home, it would be no more than I expected. We swung in the ruts, we shook like jellies on the merciless patches of broken stones, and Croppy stimulated the pace with weird whistlings through his teeth, and heavy prods with the butt of his whip in the region of the borrowed breeching.

The wind was in our teeth, and it was already raining a little, enough to justify our sagacity in leaving the river, enough to lend a touch of passion to the thought of home and Julia.

The grey horse began to lean back against the borrowed breeching, the chains of the traces clanked loosely. We had begun the long zig-zag slant down to the village.

And there, not fifty yards away, was the Dean's inside car, labouring slowly, inevitably, up to meet us. Even in that stupefying moment I was aware that the silver-banded hat of the coachman was at a most uncanonical angle. Behind me on the car was stowed my umbrella; I tore it from the retaining embrace of the landing-net, and unfurled it with the speed of light. Instantly, and without a note of warning, there came a scurry of hoofs, a grinding of wheels, and a confused out-cry of voices. A violent jerk nearly pitched me off the car, as Croppy dragged the white horse into the opposite bank ; the umbrella flew from my hand and revealed to me the Dean's coachman sitting on the road scarcely a yard from my feet, uttering large and drunken shouts while the covered car hurried back towards the village with the unfor-gettable yell of Miss McEvoy bursting from its curtained rear.

" They're dead ! They're dead ! " said Croppy, with philosophic calm ; " 'twas the parasol started him."

As he spoke, the black horse stumbled, the laden car ran on top of him like a landslip, and, bereft of the breeching that might have saved him, with an abortive flounder he collapsed upon the road. Once down, he lay, after the manner of his kind, like a dead thing, and the covered car, propped on its shafts, presented its open mouth to the heavens. Even as I sped headlong to the rescue in the wake of Robert and Croppy, I foreknew that Fate had after all been too many for us ; and when, an instant later, I seated myself in the orthodox manner upon the black horse's winker, and perceived that one of the shafts was broken, I was already, in spirit, making up beds with Julia for the reception of the party.

Croppy was firm and circumstantial in laying the blame on me and the umbrella.

" Sure, I seen the horse wondhering at it an' he comin' up the hill to us. 'Twas that turned him."

The dissertation in which the Dean's coachman made the entire disaster hinge upon the theft of the breeching was able, but cannot conveniently be here set down.

For my part, I hold with Julia.

" 'Twas Helayna Coolahan gave the dhrink to the Dane's coach-man ! There isn't another one in the place that'd do it ! I'm told the priest was near breaking his umbrella on her over it."

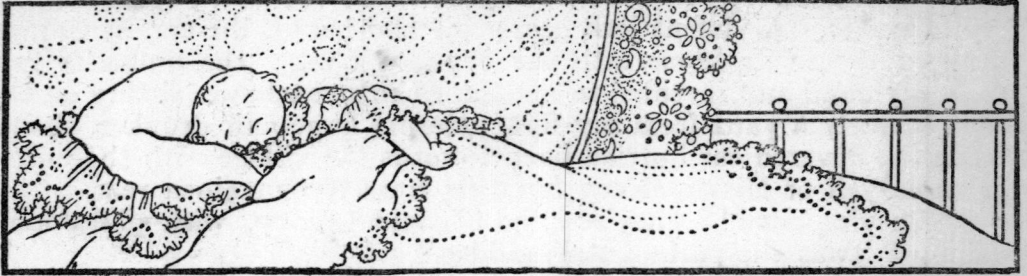

ONE YEAR OLD
By Marjory Royce

Painting by
M. E. Gray

Drawings by
Charles Robinson

AT one, the child no Christmas keeps,
So calm on Christmas Eve he sleeps,
Though, through the busy house-
hold, all
Hurry to keep the Festival.

□　　□

His Mother stands beside the bed,
Watching the little golden head,
And hangs, a little way above—
The stocking that he will not love.

□　　□

We others must do this and this—
We, who are old in Christmases;
But Baby starts, serene and gay,
Another sweet unstrenuous day.

□　　□

We who are old in Christmas lore
May miss the Vision we adore;
But Baby knows the Christ-Child well—
Sees Him, and thinks no miracle!

ONE YEAR OLD.

From a painting by M. E. Gray

WILL YOU TAKE OVER HIS HORSE, SIR?

A Tale from the Trenches by
"Sapper"

Drawings by
Edmund Blampied

In the sky overhead the sun struggled through the drifting clouds, throwing a watery gleam on the sea of mud which called itself the picket line. Just for a moment it seemed as if it would triumph, and, as I looked up, the old bay horse with the batman standing at his head was bathed in sunshine. Behind him the troop-horses steadily munching hay; the men in little scattered groups squatting round camp fires watching their dinners cook. Just the same as it was yesterday, just the same as it was the day before, but—

"Will you take over his horse, sir?"

□   □   □   □

In the distance a black speck seemed to be hanging in the air. All round it little sharp flashes of fire and fleecy puffs of smoke showed that the Germans had also seen that speck and hoped it was within range. There was one complete set of six smoke balls, so close together that one could almost cover them with a soup plate. Another set had only five. Ah! there was the sixth, a little wide. There had been three perfect groups of six when he and I had been looking at the same thing a few mornings before. Listlessly I watched the black speck. Gradually it grew larger and larger until the big biplane passed overhead. And underneath the Union Jack—painted on the plane. Just the same, thank Heaven, just the same. The flag untouched, each unit which represents that flag carrying on the inexorable work. There is no cessation; there are others; it is war, but—

"Will you take over his horse?"

□   □   □   □

The old bay horse! I wonder if you, too, remember that day at Tattersall's. Do you remember the hand running over your legs and stopping at that big splint on your off fore? Can't you hear again that voice you got to know so well? "Look at those hocks, man; look at that shoulder; that splint may just bring him down to my price." And do you remember the hunts? Do you remember that point-to-point when you both came such a crumpler at that big stake and binder? Perhaps you remember, old horse, perhaps you do;

147

for who shall say just where an animal's knowledge begins and ends ? There's no good your looking round like that. You haven't seen him this morning, have you ?—and you know something's wrong, but you don't know what. How should you ? You don't understand, and I do, Heaven knows—which is worse. In time perhaps the sugar will taste just as good out of my hand as far as you're concerned. I hope it will, because—well, you heard the question, too—

" Will you take over his horse ? "

□   □   □   □

Yes, I must take you over until some one else can take you from me, if you come through this show alive. You don't know much about that some one, do you, old chap ? Do you remember that day when you made such a fool of yourself because a side saddle had been put on you for the first time, and your master with a sack round his waist was sitting on your back all askew, as you thought. And then about a week after, when you were quite accustomed to it, some one else got upon you who was so light that you scarcely felt any weight at all. And when you lifted your heels a bit, just for fun, because you hardly knew there was any one there at all, do you remember how he rubbed your muzzle and talked to you until you became quiet ? But there are so many things that you can't know, aren't there, old horse ? You weren't in my room when he came round to it that night to tell me before any one else of his wonderful luck. You couldn't know that the little light load you carried so often was the most precious thing in the whole world to the man who never missed coming round to your box after dinner on a hunting day, to make sure you were rugged up and bedded down for the night all right. That's where I get the pull of you, old man. You see, I was going to be his best man when he could afford to get married. He insisted on that when he told me first. But—things have happened since that night, and I'm going to take you over, because I want to give you back to her. I don't expect you'll carry her hunting again ; women aren't made that way—at least not this one. Though he'd like it, I know.

□   □   □

But then, he won't be able to tell her. That's the rub. I know it was only yesterday afternoon you heard him say that it was a grand day for a hunt. I know it was only last night that you were saddled up suddenly with all the other troop-horses and trotted for two hours along muddy roads in the darkness. Then he dismounted—didn't he ?—and went on on foot with his men, while you and his other horse stopped behind. And you couldn't understand why, a few hours later, when the other men mounted, no one got on your back, and you were led back here. Just a casual German sniper, sitting in a tree, taking pot shots into the darkness. Just a small round hole right in the centre of his forehead and the back of his head—but we won't think of that. That's what happened, old man. Nothing very glorious —nothing at all heroic. It's so ordinary, isn't it ? It has already happened hundreds of times. It's going to happen hundreds more. Everything is going on just the same. It hasn't made any difference. The guns are in action just as they were yesterday, and there's that Maxim going again. But you've lost your master, old horse ; and I've lost a friend. And the girl ?—— Not a bad bag, for half an ounce of lead !

They've left him up there, with a cross over his shallow grave, and his name scrawled on it with an indelible pencil. One can't get up there in the daylight—it's not safe. I'd like to have gone to-night to see if it was all right ; but there's a job of work to be done elsewhere. So I'll have to lie to her. I'm writing her this afternoon. I can't let her open the paper one morning, and suddenly see his name standing out in letters of fire from all the others. Just a pawn in the game—another officer killed—a bare, hard fact, brutal, uncompromising. No more letters to look forward to : no more socks and smokes to send out. True, the socks never fitted, but she didn't know. No : I can't let her find it out that way. I must write : though what on earth can I say to her ? I never could write a letter like that. If you're going to have your head smashed with a sledge-hammer, one can't do much to deaden the blow. But I'll tell her I've seen his grave, and that it's all right. Just a pawn in the game. Only he was her king.

" Will you take over his horse, sir ? Your chestnut is very lame in front."

Teddy, old man, I've hunted with you ; I've shot with you ; I've played cricket with you ; I've made love with you. You were one of Nature's sportsmen—one of the salt of the earth. May the earth lie lightly on you, old pal. There's a motor-cyclist coming with orders now : the same fellow with spectacles who has been to us for the last fortnight. There's a Taube overhead, and the infantry are loosing off at it. It's out of range, just the same as usual. Everything is just the same, Teddy, except that some one's heart has got to be broken, and that I—well, I've taken over your horse.

"HE COMES!"
IN MEMORIAM "ROBERTS, F.M."

By Maud Diver

Drawings by J. H. Hartley

A WORD sped through the trenches, like flame through summer grass,
Where Sikh and Pathan and Gurkha crouch in the mud and rain,
Where Rajput and Punjabi cheer at the shells that pass,
Reckless of death or danger, eager to smite again.
" Never a war like this war, where a thousand bullets sing.
Great are the guns of the foemen ; greater the British King."

A word sped through the trenches : " Our *Jung-i-Látsahib* comes !
He, that was ' Bobs *Bahádur* ' of Kábul and Kandahar—
Unforgetting and unforgotten of us in our Indian homes—
Soldier, he greets his soldiers in thunder and flame of war—
His the will and the courage no burden of years can bend,
Victor in the beginning ; victor unto the end.

" Can we forget, who knew him in the noontide of his fame—
Worthy avenger of heroes, little and wise and bold—
When Hindostan was ringing with the glory of his name,
And we that had seen bore witness wherever the tale was told ?
Lo, neither fame, nor honours, nor years can wean his heart
From the warrior sons of India.   Hail to our *Jung-i-Lát* ! "

He came—and their eyes beheld him : changed, yet himself
    indeed ;
Still the face of their leader, though frosted with age and frail ;
Still the imperial spirit, supreme in the hour of need :
He came—and they gave him greeting : " Roberts *Bahádur*,
    hail !
Conqueror, loved and honoured from Comorin to Tibet,
Your trophy—the heart of India.   Shall India ever forget ? "

Enough that he had their greeting ; enough that he saw and
    heard
The cannon lighten and thunder, the flash and crash of the fight ;
Enough that the guns of England should speak the parting word
As he passed beyond their voices into the Greater Light :
Enough that an Empire acclaims him—soldier, patriot, friend ;
Victor in the beginning ; victor unto the end.

THE CUBHOOD OF WAHB

Written and Illustrated by
Ernest Thompson Seton

HE was born over a score of years ago, away up in the wildest part of the wild West, on the head of the Little Piney, above where the Palette Ranch is now.

His Mother was just an ordinary Silvertip, living the quiet life that all Bears prefer, minding her own business and doing her duty by her family, asking no favours of any one excepting to let her alone.

It was July before she took her remarkable family down the Little Piney to the Graybull, and showed them what strawberries were, and where to find them.

Notwithstanding their Mother's deep conviction, the cubs were not remarkably big or bright; yet they were a remarkable family, for there were four of them, and it is not often a Grizzly Mother can boast of more than two.

The woolly-coated little creatures were having a fine time, and revelled in the lovely mountain summer and the abundance of good things.

Their Mother turned over each log and flat stone they came to, and the moment it was lifted they all rushed under it like a lot of little pigs to lick up the ants and grubs there hidden.

It never once occurred to them that Mammy's strength might fail some time, and let the great rock drop just as they got under it; nor would any one have thought so that might have chanced to see that huge arm and that shoulder sliding about under the great yellow robe she wore. No, no; that arm could never fail. The little ones were quite right. So they hustled and tumbled one another at each fresh log in their haste to be first, and squealed little squeals, and growled little growls, as if each were a pig, a pup, and a kitten all rolled into one.

They were well acquainted with the common little brown ants that harbour under logs in the uplands, but now they came for the first time on one of the hills of the great, fat, luscious Wood-ant, and they all crowded around to lick up those that ran out.

151

But they soon found that they were licking up more cactus-prickles and sand than ants, till their Mother said in Grizzly, " Let me show you how."

She knocked off the top of the hill, then laid her great paw flat on it for a few moments, and as the angry ants swarmed on to it she licked them up with one lick, and got a good rich mouthful to crunch, without a grain of sand or a cactus-stinger in it.

The cubs soon learned.   Each put up both his little brown paws, so that there was a ring of paws all around the ant-hill, and there they sat, like children playing "hands," and each licked first the right and then the left paw, or one cuffed his brother's ears for licking a paw that was not his own, till the ant-hill was cleared out and they were ready for a change.

Ants are sour food and made the Bears thirsty, so the old one led down to the river.   After they had drunk as much as they wanted, and dabbled their feet, they walked down the bank to a pool, where the old one's keen eye caught sight of a number of Buffalo-fish basking on the bottom.   The water was very low, mere pebbly rapids between these deep holes, so Mammy said to the little ones :

" Now you all sit there on the bank and learn something new."

First she went to the lower end of the pool and stirred up a cloud of mud which hung in the still water, and sent a long tail floating like a curtain over the rapids just below.   Then she went quietly round by land, and sprang into the upper end of the pool with all the noise she could.

The fish had crowded to that end, but this sudden attack sent them off in a panic, and they dashed blindly into the mud-cloud.   Out of fifty fish there is always a good chance of some being fools, and half a dozen of these dashed through the darkened water into the current, and before they knew it they were struggling over the shingly shallow.   The old Grizzly jerked them out to the bank, and the little ones rushed noisily on these funny, short snakes that could not get away, and gobbled and gorged till their little bodies looked like balloons.

They had eaten so much now, and the sun was so hot, that all were quite sleepy.   So the Mother-bear led them to a quiet little nook, and as soon as she lay down, though they were puffing with heat, they all snuggled around her and went to sleep, with their little brown paws curled in, and their little black noses tucked into their wool as though it were a very cold day.

After an hour or two they began to yawn and stretch themselves, except little Fuzz, the smallest ; she poked

out her sharp nose for a moment, then snuggled back between her Mother's great arms, for she was a gentle, petted little thing.

The largest, the one afterward known as Wahb, sprawled over on his back and began to worry a root that stuck up, grumbling to himself as he chewed it, or slapped it with his paw for not staying where he wanted it.

Presently Mooney, the mischief, began tugging at Frizzle's ears, and got his own well boxed. They clenched for a tussle; then, locked in a tight little grizzly yellow ball, they sprawled over and over on the grass, and, before they knew it, down a bank, and away out of sight toward the river.

Almost immediately there was an outcry of yells for help from the little wrestlers. There could be no mistaking the real terror in their voices. Some dreadful danger was threatening.

Up jumped the gentle Mother, changed into a perfect demon, and over the bank in time to see a huge Range-bull make a deadly charge at what he doubtless took for a yellow dog.

In a moment all would have been over with Frizzle, for he had missed his footing on the bank; but there was a thumping of heavy feet, a roar that startled even the great Bull, and, like a huge bounding ball of yellow fur, Mother Grizzly was upon him. Him! the monarch of the herd, the master of all these plains, what had he to fear? He bellowed his deep war-cry, and charged to pin the old one to the bank; but as he bent to tear her with his shining horns, she dealt him a stunning blow, and before he could recover she was on his shoulders, raking the flesh from his ribs with sweep after sweep of her terrific claws.

The Bull roared with rage, and plunged and reared, dragging Mother Grizzly with him; then, as he hurled heavily off the slope, she let go to save herself, and the Bull rolled down into the river.

This was a lucky thing for him, for the Grizzly did not want to follow him there; so he waded out on the other side, and bellowing with fury and pain, slunk off to join the herd to which he belonged.

THE LITTLE GOATHERD · By Mrs. Humphry Ward

Painting by Dudley Hardy, R.I. Drawings by Leopold Bates

It was in the spring of 1899 that this tale of Nemi was written. It was composed in the old Villa Barberini, on the skirts of Castel Gandolfo, where we arrived that year in early March, and spent three enchanting months. The villa indeed gave us at first a rough welcome. In spite of our puny efforts with fires and stoves, the chill of winter, Horace's *bruma iners*, met us in all the great bare rooms ; outside, the olives and the camellias drooped under snow. The kitchen was fifty steps below the dining-room, in some cavernous den whence emerged a fierce-eyed Neapolitan cook, who filled us with vague alarms ; and the supply of all the necessaries of life seemed unreasonably small. We sat down rather sadly to our first meal, wondering whether we could stay it out. But with the night, the snow vanished and the sun emerged. We ran east to one balcony, and saw the light blazing on the Alban Lake, and had but to cross the apartment to find ourselves with all the Campagna at our feet, sparkling in a thousand colours to the sea. And outside was the garden, with its lemon-trees growing in vast jars—like the jars of Knossos—but marked with Barberini bees ; its white and red camellias be-carpeting the soft grass with their fallen petals ; its dark and tragic recesses, where melancholy trees hung above piled fragments of the great Domitian villa whose ruins lay everywhere beneath our feet ; its olive-gardens sloping to the west, and open to the sun, open too to white, nibbling goats, and wandering *bambini* ; its magical glimpse of St. Peter's to the north, through a notch in a group of stone-pines ; and last and best, its marvellous terrace that roofed a crypto-porticus of the old villa, whence the whole vast landscape, from Ostia and the mountains of Viterbo to the Circæan promontory, might be discerned, where one might sit and watch the sunsets burn in scarlet and purple through the wide west into the shining bosom of the Tyrrhenian sea.

Our spirits leapt. What a lovely sharp strangeness in it all !—an Italian austerity, caught from the chill March weather, but still rich and splendid ;—how different from that Westmoreland austerity I had tried to interweave with the story of " Helbeck " ! The three happy months rushed too quickly through. We saw the Campagna doff its winter dress, and the summer throw great splashes of yellow marigolds and scarlet poppies across its billowing green ; we made expeditions to Ninfa, to Viterbo, to Caprarola ; above all we haunted Nemi, and the niched site of its vanished temple. We were indeed only three or four miles from that wonderful volcanic lake, where Caligula's galleys still lie buried, and from the fields of *fragole* under which sleep the foundations and remains of that famous shrine of Artemis, which was still served in Caligula's day by

> The priest who slew the Slayer,
> And shall himself be slain.

As to the meaning of the Nemi legend, and its connection with some of the most primitive beliefs of mankind, let those who wish to learn take down Sir John Fraser's *Golden Bough*. They will find there all they want to know. But in *Eleanor*, the book that I was writing that spring, the tale of Quintus, the little goatherd, is a story within a story. It is supposed to be an extract from the book on Italy by Edward Manisty, the chief male figure—no one could call him the hero !—of the novel of *Eleanor*. He reads it aloud to Eleanor Burgoyne and Lucy Foster, the two contrasted women of the book. They also are staying on the Alban ridge, and Nemi is close by. Lucy Foster, the untravelled, immature, but finely-wrought American girl, is listening for the first time to Manisty's " full, over-rich voice," calling up before her a little morning scene in the hut of a Latian peasant-farmer, under Tiberius. The tale opens with the waking at dawn of the herdsman Cæculus and his little son, in their round thatched cottage on the ridge of Aricia, beneath the Alban Mount. It showed the countryman stepping out of his bed into the darkness, groping for the embers on the hearth, relighting his lamp, and calling to his boy who is still asleep on his bed of leaves. One by one the rustic facts emerged, so old, so ever new :—Cæculus grinding his corn, and singing at his work—the baking of the flat wheaten cakes on the hot embers—the gathering of herbs from the garden—the kneading them with a little cheese and oil to make a relish for the day—the harnessing of the white steers under the thonged yoke—the man going forth to his ploughing, under the mounting dawn, clad in his goatskin tunic and his leathern hat—the boy loosening the goats from their pen beside the hut, and sleepily driving them past the furrows where his father is at work, to the misty woods beyond.

Thus, with every touch, the earlier world revived, grew plainer in the sun, till Lucy Foster found herself walking in a dream with Manisty through paths that cut the Alban Hills in the days of Rome's first imperial glory, as she listened to his tale of the goatherd and Nemi.

" So the boy—Quintus—left the ploughed lands, and climbed a hill above the sleeping town. And when he reached the summit, he paused, and turned him to the west.

The Latian plain spreads beneath him in the climbing sun; at its edge is the sea in a light of pearl; the white fishing-boats sparkle along the shore. Close at his feet runs a straight road high upon the hill. He can see the country-folk on their laden mules and donkeys journeying along it, journeying northwards to the city in the plain that the spurs of the mountain hide from him. His fancy goes with them, along the Appian Way, trotting with the mules. When will his father take him again to Rome to see the shops, and the Forum, and the new white temples, and Cæsar's great palace on the hill?

Then carelessly his eyes pass southward, and there beneath him in its hollow is the lake—the round blue lake that Diana loves, where are her temple and her shadowy grove. The morning mists lie wreathed above it; the just-leafing trees stand close in the great cup; only a few patches of roof and column reveal the shrine.

On he moves. His wheaten cake is done. He takes his pipe from his girdle, touches it, and sings.

His bare feet as he moves tread down the wet flowers. Round him throng the goats; suddenly he throws down his pipe, he runs to a goat heavy with milk; he presses the teats with his quick hands; the milk flows foaming into the wooden cup he has placed below; he drinks, his brown curls sweeping the cup; then he picks up his pipe and walks on proudly before his goats, his lithe body swaying from side to side as he moves, dancing to the music that he makes. The notes float up into the morning air; the echo of them runs round the shadowy hollow of the lake.

Down trips the boy, parting the dewy branches with his brown shoulders. Around him the mountain side is golden with the broom; at his feet the white cistus covers the rock. The shrubs of the scattered wood send out their scents, and the goats browse upon their shoots.

But the path sinks gently downward, winding along the basin of the lake. And now the boy emerges from the wood; he stands upon a knoll to rest.

Ah! sudden and fierce comes the sun!—and there below him in the rich hollow it strikes the temple—Diana's temple and her grove. Out flame the white columns, the bronze roof, the white enclosing walls. Piercingly white the holy and famous place shines among the olives and the fallows: the sun burns upon the marble; Phœbus salutes his great sister. And in the waters of the lake reappear the white columns; the blue waves dance around the shimmering lines; the mists part above them; they rise from the lake, lingering awhile upon the woods.

The boy lays his hands to his eyes and looks eagerly towards the temple. Nothing. No living creature stirs.

Often has he been warned by his father not to venture alone within the grove of the goddess. Twice, indeed, on the great June festivals has he witnessed the solemn sacrifices, and the crowds of worshippers, and the torches mirrored in the lake. But without his father fear has hitherto stayed his steps far from the temple.

To-day, however, as the sun mounts, and the fresh breeze breaks from the sea, his youth and the wildness of it dance within his blood. He and his goats pass into an olive garden. The red-brown earth has been freshly turned amid the twisted trunks : the goats scatter, search-

ing for the patches of daisied grass still left by the plough. Guiltily the boy looks round him—peers through the olives and their silvery foam of leaves, as they fall past him down the steep. Then like one of his own kids he lowers his head and runs ; he leaves his flock under the olives ; he slips into a dense ilex-wood, still chill with the morning ; he presses towards its edge ; panting he climbs a huge and ancient tree that flings its boughs forward above the temple wall ; he creeps along a branch among the thick small leaves,—he lifts his head.

The temple is before him, and the sacred grove. He sees the great terrace, stretching to the lake ; he hears the little waves splashing on its buttressed wall.

Close beneath him, towards the rising and the midday sun, there stretches a great niched wall girdling the temple on two sides, each niche a shrine, and in each shrine a cold white form that waits the sun—Apollo the Far-Darter, and the spear-bearing Pallas, and among them that golden Cæsar, of whom the country talks, who has given great gifts to the temple—he and his grandson, the young Gaius.

The boy strains his eye to see, and as the light strikes into the niche, flames on the gleaming breastplate and the uplifted hand, he trembles on his branch for fear. Hurriedly he turns his look on the dwellings of the priestesses, where all still sleeps; on the rows of shining pillars that stand round about the temple; on the close-set trees of the grove that stands between it and the lake.

Hark!—a clanging of metal—of great doors upon their hinges. From the inner temple, from the shrine of the goddess, there comes a man. His head is bound with the priest's fillet; sharply the sun touches his white pointed cap; in his hand he carries a sword.

Between the temple and the grove there is a space of dazzling light. The man passes into it, turns himself to the east, and raises his hand to his mouth; drawing his robe over his head, he sinks upon the ground, and prostrate there, adores the coming god.

His prayer lasts but an instant. Rising in haste, he stands, looking around him, his sword gathered in his hand. He is a man still young; his stature is more than the ordinary height of men; his limbs are strong and supple. His rich dress, moreover, shows him to be both priest and king. But again the boy among his leaves draws his trembling body close, hiding, like a lizard when some passing step has startled it from the sun. For on this haggard face the gods have written strange and terrible things; the priest's eyes deep-sunk under his shaggy hair dart from side to side in a horrible unrest; he seems a creature separate from his kind—possessed of evil—dedicate to fear.

In the midst of the temple grove stands one vast ilex—the tree of trees, sacred to Trivia. The other trees fall back from it in homage; and round it paces the priest, alone in the morning light.

But his is no holy meditation. His head is thrown back; his ear listens for every sound; the bared sword glitters as he moves. . . .

There is a rustle among the further trees. Quickly the boy stretches his brown neck; for at the sound the priest crouches on himself; he throws the robe from his right arm, and so waits, ready to strike.

The light falls on his pale features, the torment of his brow, the anguish of his drawn lips. Beside the lapping lake, and under the golden morning, he stands as Terror in the midst of Peace.

Silence again;—only the questing birds call from the olive-woods. Panting, the priest moves onward, racked with sick tremors, prescient of doom.

But hark! a cry!—and yet another answering—a dark form bursting from the grove—a fierce locked struggle under the sacred tree. The boy crawls to the farthest end of the branch, his eyes starting from his head.

From the temple enclosure, from the farther trees, from the

THE LITTLE GOATHERD.

From a painting by Dudley Hardy, R.I.

hill around, a crowd comes running; men and white-robed priestesses, women, children even—gathering in haste. But they pause afar off. Not a living soul approaches the place of combat; not a hand gives aid. The boy can see the faces of the virgins who serve the temple. They are pale, but very still. Not a sound of pity escapes their white lips; their ambiguous eyes watch calmly for the issue of the strife.

And on the farther side, at the edge of the grove, stand country-folk, men in goatskin tunics and leathern hats like the boy's father. And the little goatherd, not knowing what he does, calls to them for help in his shrill voice. But no one heeds; and the priest himself calls no one, entreats no one.

Ah! The priest wavers—he falls—his white robes are in the dust. The bright steel rises—descends;—the last groan speeds to heaven.

The victor raised himself from the dead, all stained with the blood and soil of the battle. Quintus gazed upon him astonished. For here was no rude soldier, nor swollen boxer, but a youth merely—a youth, slender and beautiful, fair-haired and of a fair complexion. His loins were girt with a slave's tunic. Pallid were his young features; his limbs wasted with hunger and toil; his eyes blood-streaked as those of the deer when the dogs close upon its tender life.

And looking down upon the huddled priest, fallen in his blood upon the dust, he peered long into the dead face, as though he beheld it for the first time. Shudders ran through him; Quintus listened to hear him weep or moan. But at the last he lifted his head fiercely, straightening his limbs like one who reminds himself of black fate, and things not to be undone. And turning to the multitude, he made a sign. With shouting and wild cries they came upon him; they snatched the purple-striped robe from the murdered priest, and with it they clothed his murderer. They put on him the priest's fillet and the priest's cap; they hung garlands upon his neck; and with rejoicing and obeisance they led him to the sacred temple. . . .

And for many hours more the boy remained hidden in the tree, held there by the spell of his terror. He saw the temple ministers take up the body of the dead, and carelessly drag it from the grove. All day long was there crowd and festival within the sacred precinct. But when the shadows began to fall from the ridge of Aricia across the lake; when the new-made priest had offered on Trivia's altar a white steer, nourished on the Alban grass; when he had fed the fire of Vesta, and poured offerings to Virbius the immortal, whom in ancient days great Diana had snatched from the gods' wrath and hidden there, safe within the Arician wood,—when these were done, the crowd departed and the Grove-King came forth alone from the temple.

The boy watched what he would do. In his hand he carried the sword, which at the sunrise he had taken from the dead. And he came to the sacred tree that was in the middle of the grove, and he too began to pace about it, glancing from side to side, as that other had done before him. And once, when he was near the place where the caked blood still lay upon the ground, the sword fell clashing from his hand, and he flung his two arms to heaven with a hoarse and piercing cry—the cry of him who accuses and arraigns the gods.

And the boy, shivering, slipped from the tree, with that cry in his ear, and hastily sought for his goats. And when he had found them he drove them home, not staying even to quench his thirst from their swollen udders. And in the shepherd's hut he found his father Cæculus; and sinking down beside him with tears and sobs, he told his tale.

And Cæculus pondered long. And, without chiding, he laid his hand upon the boy's head, and bade him be comforted. 'For,' said he, as though he spake with himself—'such is the will of the goddess. And from the farthest times it has happened thus—before the Roman fathers journeyed from the Alban Mount and made them dwellings on the seven hills—before Romulus gave laws—or any white-robed priest had climbed the Capitol. From blood springs up the sacred office; and to blood it goes! No natural death must waste the priest of Trivia's tree. The earth is hungry for the blood in its strength— nor shall it be withheld! Thus only do the trees bear and the fields bring forth.'

Astonished, the boy looked at his father, and saw upon his face, as he turned it upon the ploughed lands and the vineyards, a secret and a savage joy. And the little goatherd's mind was filled with terror— nor would his father tell him further what the mystery meant. But when he went to his bed of dried leaves at night, and the moon rose upon the lake, and the great woods murmured in the hollow far beneath him, he tossed restlessly from side to side, thinking of the new priest who kept watch there—of his young limbs and miserable eyes —of that voice which he had flung to heaven. And the child tried to believe that he might yet escape. But already in his dreams he saw the grove part once more and the slayer leap forth. He saw watching crowd — and their fierce, steady eyes, waiting thirstily for the spilt blood. And it was as though a mighty hand crushed the boy's heart, and for the first time he shrank from the gods, and from his father,—so that the joy of his youth was dark-ened within him."